THE TIMES
TOP 100
GRADUATE EMPLOYERS

The essential guide to the leading employers recruiting graduates in 1999-2000.

HIGH FLIERS

HIGH FLIERS PUBLICATIONS LTD
IN ASSOCIATION WITH THE TIMES

Published by High Fliers Publications Limited
10a Belmont Street, Camden Town, London NW1 8HH
Telephone 0207 428 9000

Edited by Martin Birchall & Louisa Allen

Portrait Photography by Ben Schott.
Cartoons by Kevin Flannery.

Printed and bound in Great Britain.

A CIP catalogue record for this book
is available from the British Library.

ISBN 0 9536991 0 2

Contents

LINACRE COLLEGE
WITHDRAWN

Foreword

*by **Peter Stothard***
Editor of The Times

Welcome to the first edition of *The Times Top 100 Graduate Employers* directory. Defining which organisations offer the 'best' careers for graduates is no easy task.

The choice of employment for final year students leaving university in the year 2000 has never been greater. There are well over 1,000 major employers who actively recruit graduates from UK universities, and countless smaller organisations who employ recent graduates within their workforce. At many of the universities that are most popular with employers, up to 150 different companies are expected to hold recruitment presentations or take part in campus careers fairs.

How then can such a huge number of employers be assessed and ranked? We turned to the 'Class of 1999' and interviewed more than 11,000 final year students at universities across the UK, to find out which organisations they believed offered the best opportunities for graduates.

Their responses produced a list of over 800 different employers, covering every possible employment sector and business type - from oil companies to specialist IT firms, manufacturers of household goods to government departments, well-known accountancy firms to leading investment banks. The one hundred employers who were mentioned most often form *The Times Top 100 Graduate Employers*.

The result is a definitive guide to the employers who are judged to provide the brightest prospects for graduates. Whether by the quality of their training programmes, the business success that they enjoy, the scale of their organisations, or by the impression their recruitment activities have made, these are the employers that are most attractive to graduates in 1999.

The Times Top 100 Graduate Employers directory will not necessarily identify which employer is right for you: only you can decide that. But the directory is an ideal starting point if you want to discover how many of these leading employers recruit their graduates. It provides details of their graduate programmes, the functions they recruit for, and when to make applications.

Choosing a career and finding a job can be a daunting prospect, but it is one of the most important decisions you will ever take. Being well-informed is a good first step.

You spend 3 years getting a degree.

Don't spend the same time getting a job.

PUT YOURSELF IN THE PICTURE WITH
OUR GRADUATE CAREERS SECTION.

EVERY MONDAY.

THE TIMES

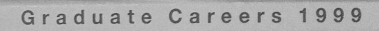
Graduate Careers 1999

Compiling the Top 100 Graduate Employers

*by **Martin Birchall***
Survey Director of High Fliers Research Limited

More than five thousand UK and international organisations are believed to be looking to recruit graduates in 1999-2000. The choice of employer has never been greater, so if you are in your final year or have just left university, now is a buoyant time to look for work.

But all this choice makes finding the 'right' employer much more difficult. How can you decide which employers offer the 'best' graduates jobs? What criteria can you use to differentiate between so many organisations and opportunities?

There are no simple answers to these questions and clearly no one employer can ever hope to be right for every graduate. Everyone makes their own judgements about the employers they want to work for and types of job they find the most attractive.

How, then, can anyone produce a meaningful league table of the leading employers? What criteria can define whether one organisation is 'better' than another? Well, to compile *The Times Top 100 Graduate Employers*, the independent market research company, High Fliers Research Ltd, interviewed 11,427 final year students due to graduate from UK universities in the summer of 1999. The students from the 'Class of 1999' who took part in the study were selected at random to represent the full cross-section of finalists at their universities, not just those who had

found employment or had decided on their careers. The research examined students' experiences during their search for a graduate job and asked them about their attitudes to employers.

The key question used to produce the *Top 100*, was "Which employer do you think offers the best opportunities for graduates?" This was an open-ended question and students were not prompted or directed in any way for their answers. Incredibly, across the whole survey, finalists mentioned more than 800 different organisations - from the smallest local employers to some of the world's best known companies. The responses were analysed to identify the number of times each employer was mentioned. The one hundred organisations that were mentioned most often are the *Top 100* graduate employers for 1999.

It is clear from the huge selection of answers given by finalists in the 'Class of 1999' that individual students used very different criteria to determine which employer they considered offered the best opportunities for graduates. Some focused on employers' general reputations - their public image, their business profile or their commercial success. These views were often greatly coloured by the media or students' experiences as consumers, and finalists used these impressions to define what they thought of the organisations as potential employers.

Others evaluated employers based on the

THE TOP 100 - THE TOP GRADUATE EMPLOYERS IN 1999

Rank	Company	Rank	Company
1.	Andersen Consulting	51.	Linklaters
2.	Arthur Andersen	52.	Data Connection
3.	PricewaterhouseCoopers	53.	Allen & Overy
4.	Procter & Gamble	54.	J Sainsbury
5.	Civil Service	55.	Foreign Office
6.	British Airways	56.	Royal Navy
7.	Marks & Spencer	57.	Police
8.	KPMG	58.	Microsoft
9.	Unilever	59.	McDonalds
10.	Boots	60.	Citibank
11.	Ford	61.	Standard Life
12.	GlaxoWellcome	62.	Eversheds
13.	Ernst & Young	63.	Rolls-Royce
14.	BBC	64.	Bank of England
15.	Army	65.	Natwest Bank
16.	Deloitte & Touche	66.	Virgin
17.	IBM	67.	Saatchi & Saatchi
18.	Mars	68.	Peugeot
19.	Esso	69.	Hewlett Packard
20.	BP	70.	British Steel
21.	Shell	71.	Mott Macdonald
22.	McKinsey & Co	72.	Marakon Associates
23.	British Aerospace	73.	Cable & Wireless
24.	Kingfisher	74.	Abbey National
25.	Goldman Sachs	75.	United Biscuits
26.	AstraZeneca	76.	Sony
27.	NHS	77.	Salomon Smith Barney
28.	J.P. Morgan	78.	Oliver, Wyman & Co
29.	HSBC	79.	Norton Rose
30.	BT	80.	European Union
31.	Pfizer	81.	Deutsche Bank
32.	Warburg Dillon Read	82.	Walkers Snack Foods
33.	Clifford Chance	83.	Smithkline Beecham
34.	Barclays Bank	84.	Royal Bank of Scotland
35.	Schroders	85.	PA Consulting
36.	Schlumberger	86.	Nortel
37.	Reuters	87.	Mitchell Madison
38.	Ove Arup	88.	EDS
39.	Logica	89.	Druid
40.	GKN	90.	Boston Consulting
41.	Bass	91.	BNFL
42.	Chase	92.	Slaughter & May
43.	L'Oreal	93.	Phillips
44.	DERA	94.	P&O
45.	RAF	95.	DESG
46.	Nestle	96.	Credit Suisse
47.	Lloyds TSB	97.	Capital One
48.	Merrill Lynch	98.	British Sugar
49.	John Lewis	99.	Bank of Scotland
50.	ICI	100.	Tesco

Source - *Graduate Careers Survey 1999*, High Fliers Research Ltd

11,427 final year students leaving UK universities in the summer of 1999 were asked 'Which employer do you think offers the best opportunities for graduates?' The companies mentioned most often appear in the 'Top 100'.

information they had seen during their job search - the quality of their recruitment promotions, the impression they had formed from meeting employers when they visited universities, or their experiences through the recruitment and selection process. Finalists also considered the numbers of vacancies that organisations were recruiting for as an indicator of graduates' prospects, or were influenced by an employer's profile on campus.

However, many used the 'employment proposition' as their main guide - the quality of graduate training & development that an employer promises, the remuneration package available, and the practical aspects of a first job such as location or working hours.

Regardless of the criteria that students used to arrive at their answer, the hardest part for many was just selecting a single organisation - choosing two or three, or even half a dozen employers, in many ways would have been much easier. But the whole purpose of the exercise was to replicate the reality that everyone faces - you can only work for one organisation and at each stage of the job search there are choices to be made as to which direction to take and which employers to pursue.

The resulting Top 100 is a dynamic league table of the UK's most exciting and well-respected graduate recruiters. It is headed by the management consultancy firm, Andersen Consulting, who although were not the largest recruiter of graduates in 1999, certainly had a particularly high 'on-campus' profile at many major UK universities. In the league table, the firm was mentioned by nearly 5% of all students interviewed for the research.

Four other recruiters - Arthur Andersen, one of the 'Big Five' accountancy and professional services firms; PricewaterhouseCoopers, the firm created by the merger of Price Waterhouse and Coopers & Lybrand in 1998; Procter & Gamble, the international fast moving consumer goods company; and the Civil Service - enjoy a very clear lead ahead of other graduate employers, and almost a fifth of all finalists questioned named one of the top five organisations. Other successful employers who appear within the first ten include British Airways, Marks & Spencer, KPMG, Unilever, and Boots.

No one type of employer dominates the *Top 100*, although all of the 'Big Five' accountancy and professional services firms appear in the top twenty. Many of the best-known employment sectors feature strongly - industry, banking, retailing, pharmaceuticals, law, telecommunications, IT and consultancy.

There appears to be little correlation between the number of graduates an employer recruits and where they appear in the *Top 100*. The

THE TOP 100 - FACTS & FIGURES

Within the *Top 100*, there are organisations from almost every major employment sector, between them offering more than 15,000 graduate jobs each year. By way of an illustration of the variety of jobs available from these employers, look out for the following organisations:

- **22** industrial or manufacturing companies
- **17** retailers, high street banks or finance companies
- **12** public sector organisations
- **11** investment banks
- **9** FMCG companies
- **9** specialist IT hardware or software companies
- **9** consultancies
- **6** law firms
- **5** major accountancy and professional service firms

"So, all those years of study have finally been worth it."

majority of organisations listed in the table recruit 50 graduates or less each year, but there are at least twenty employers who recruit in excess of 300 graduates annually. Britain's largest employer of graduates is currently PricewaterhouseCoopers, who recruited an estimated 1,400 during 1998-9, and although they appear close to the top of the table, they are not in first place.

There are a further three organisations who take on 1,000 or more recruits and only one of these is in the top five. Furthermore, there are several major employers who have an annual intake of at least 500 graduates who are not listed within the top thirty employers. Conversely, three employers had vacancies for less than 100 graduates and appeared in the top twenty. It is clear that sheer volume of graduate vacancies is not enough to influence students' employment choices.

Money is not an indicator either. The employers who offer the highest salaries and the best sign-up packages are not necessarily the organisations that are rated most highly. Equally, many of the employers offering average or below average salaries are ranked amongst the top organisations. Understandably then, there is no single factor which seems to determine an employer's position in the league.

Overall, more than 40% of the 'Class of 1999' mentioned the organisations that form the top fifty employers, whilst the full *Top 100* accounted for the choices of just under half of the final year population. This underlines how a relatively small proportion of the total number of employers who seek to recruit graduates dominate finalists' preferences.

Other parts of the research provide useful pointers as to the employment choices that the finalists of 1999 made. When asked about the sectors that they had made applications to or would be applying to during their job search, the top destination was management consultancy. Nearly one in seven of finalists had sought graduate jobs in this sector, making it one of the most competitive areas in the graduate job market. Almost equally popular were careers in marketing and the media, although the availability of graduate positions varied considerably. Many of the marketing positions that finalists applied for

THE TOP 100 - LEADING CAREER DESTINATIONS FOR GRADUATES IN 1999

Rank	Career Sector	% who wanted jobs in the sector	Rank	Career Sector	% who wanted jobs in the sector
1.	Management Consultancy	14.1	11.	Civil Service	9.2
2.	Marketing	13.5	12.	Charity or Voluntary Work	8.8
3.	Media	12.0	13.	Investment Banking	8.6
4.	Research & Development	11.6	14.	Human Resources	8.0
5.	Accountancy	10.7	15.	Sales	6.3
6.	Computing & IT	10.5	16.	Law	6.1
7.	General Management	10.4	17.	Retailing	5.0
8.	Engineering	9.8	18.	Armed Forces	2.7
9.	Teaching	9.7	19.	Purchasing	2.3
10.	Finance	9.6	20.	Police	1.7

Source - *Graduate Careers Survey 1999*, High Fliers Research Ltd

11,427 final year students leaving UK universities in the summer of 1999 were asked which career sectors had they already applied to or were likely to apply to during their search for a graduate job.

were promoted whilst they were still at university, but the vast majority of media jobs were advertised during the summer after graduation.

The other sectors attracting large numbers of applications include research & development, accountancy, IT and general management. Despite the keen demand for qualified graduates, less than 10% of finalists applied for jobs in engineering, and up to a fifth of those studying on engineering courses opted for careers in other sectors.

Finalists were also asked about the type of employer they would most like to work for. The top choice for almost half of those questioned was a 'national or international company', reflecting perhaps the profile of companies who had visited universities across the UK during the recruitment round. These larger employers dramatically outnumber smaller recruiters at most universities by virtue of their greater resources and the scale of their graduate recruitment programmes.

Despite this, one in seven finalists said they would prefer to work in a small or medium sized firm, a similar number wanted a position within the public sector, and 11% were keen to work for themselves either by running their own business or by freelancing. The less popular options were to work in an academic institution, an artistic company or within the voluntary sector.

These choices are broadly confirmed by the organisations who appear within the *Top 100* graduate employers. Twelve of the organisations are public sector and a similar number are smaller commercial companies. Across the full sample of organisations that finalists of 1999 mentioned, artistic and academic or voluntary sector organisations are well represented.

The Times Top 100 Graduate Employers directory is a celebration of the very best organisations that are recruiting today. It is a recognition of the success that these employers found with 1999's finalists and as such, is a useful indicator for the next generation of job hunters.

The league table is fluid and without doubt, next year's *Top 100* may well look very different. The graduate market remains a complex one and the challenge for the 'Class of 2000' will be to unravel the world of opportunity that it represents.

THE TOP 100 - PREFERRED TYPE OF EMPLOYER IN 1999

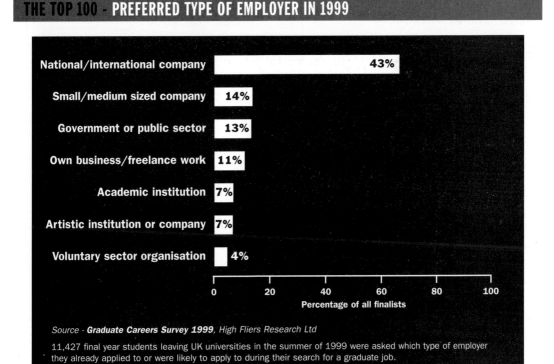

Source - **Graduate Careers Survey 1999**, High Fliers Research Ltd

11,427 final year students leaving UK universities in the summer of 1999 were asked which type of employer they already applied to or were likely to apply to during their search for a graduate job.

THE TOP 100 - USING THIS DIRECTORY

Many of the employers who appear within *The Times Top 100 Graduate Employers* are featured in the 'Employer Entries' section of the directory. These entries describe what each organisation does, the opportunities they offer graduates, and practical details about their recruitment programme for 1999-2000.

Each entry follows a standard format and contains two main elements - descriptive text and an employer fact file:

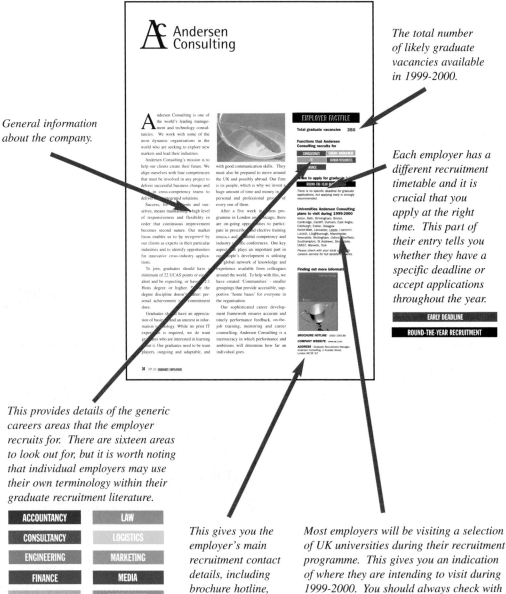

The total number of likely graduate vacancies available in 1999-2000.

General information about the company.

Each employer has a different recruitment timetable and it is crucial that you apply at the right time. This part of their entry tells you whether they have a specific deadline or accept applications throughout the year.

This provides details of the generic careers areas that the employer recruits for. There are sixteen areas to look out for, but it is worth noting that individual employers may use their own terminology within their graduate recruitment literature.

ACCOUNTANCY	LAW
CONSULTANCY	LOGISTICS
ENGINEERING	MARKETING
FINANCE	MEDIA
GENERAL MANAGEMENT	PURCHASING
HUMAN RESOURCES	RESEARCH & DEVELOPMENT
INVESTMENT BANKING	RETAILING
IT	SALES

This gives you the employer's main recruitment contact details, including brochure hotline, website and postal address.

Most employers will be visiting a selection of UK universities during their recruitment programme. This gives you an indication of where they are intending to visit during 1999-2000. You should always check with your careers service to see if the employer will be attending a local careers fair or holding a presentation at your university.

Looking for a career that will suit you?

It's all about making an impact.

If you want a lively and challenging career that will fulfil your potential while keeping your options open, you should be talking to us about business and IT consulting.

Andersen Consulting can offer you an unparalleled range of innovative and flexible career opportunities. Imagine what you could accomplish at one of the world's leading management and technology consulting organisations.

Our clients recognise that Andersen Consulting offers the unique ability to align strategy with people, processes and technology - an approach that transforms visionary ideas into successful working realities. You'd team with some of the most successful organisations - those seeking sustainable profound change, exploring new markets, leading their industries and creating their futures.

Andersen Consulting has an outstanding reputation for training and career development. We ensure that all our employees are equipped with the skills that provide the foundation of a fulfilling career, and in our meritocratic organisation, promotion is never very far away. You would join a community of professionals which has a particularly strong family spirit and provides constant support. Working at Andersen Consulting is all about teamwork and sharing of knowledge - developing relationships with colleagues and clients alike.

You won't have routine days at Andersen Consulting. You'll work in a dynamic, intellectually interesting environment, helping to make changes essential to a client's success. You will be able to make the most of your analytical skills, flexibility and resilience, working alongside like-minded and highly talented people.

Isn't this what you've been looking for in a career? To find out more about Andersen Consulting, please contact the Careers Service or call our recruiting helpline free on 0500 100189. You can also visit our Web site at www.ac.com

AC Andersen Consulting

THE TOP 100 - FINDING OUT MORE ABOUT THE EMPLOYERS

Enter our free prize draw to win a Ford Ka, worth nearly £7,000!

Use our FREE brochure and application form request service to find out more about any of the graduate employers featured within *The Times Top 100 Graduate Employers* directory, and you could be driving a brand new car to work when you start your first job!

All you need to do is complete the special **Information Request Card** that appears opposite and send it back to us before **Friday 7th January 2000**. Every completed request card or coupon will be entered into a special prize draw to win a brand new **Ford Ka**, complete with 1.3 sefi engine, power steering, a driver's airbag and a 1000 radio/cassette.

The brochures and application forms that you request will be despatched to you from the employers directly, and you should receive the information you want within a few days. The service is entirely free to all UK students and will continue to operate until 31st March 2000.

The first 1,000 requests received will win a special-edition mug from The Times Top 100 Graduate Employers directory.

Terms and Conditions for the Prize Draw - 1. Entry to this Prize Draw will be on receipt of a completed Information Request Card.   2. Entries are limited to one per person, no purchase necessary.   3. The Prize Draw is open to all UK residents aged 18 or over studying on a full-time degree course at a UK university or college of higher education. Employees of Ford Motor Company Ltd, High Fliers Publications Ltd, Times Newspapers Ltd, its associated companies, dealers or agents directly associated with this Prize Draw.   4. The Prize Draw will take place on Friday 7th January 2000 under independent supervision and the winner will be notified in writing. No correspondence will be entered into concerning this Prize Draw.   5. The first entry drawn will receive a Ford Ka 1.3 sefi engine with power steering, driver's airbag, engine immobiliser with a 1000 radio/cassette.   6. The prize is not transferable and no cash alternative is available.   7. The winner's entry to the Prize Draw assumes the winner consents to participation in High Fliers Publications Ltd, Times Newspapers Ltd and Ford Motor Company Ltd promotional publicity about this Prize Draw. 8. The promoter is: High Fliers Publications Ltd, 10a Belmont Street, Camden Town, London NW1 8HH.

THE TIMES

TOP 100
GRADUATE EMPLOYERS

Find out more about Britain's top graduate employers and you could start your career driving a brand new car!

INFORMATION REQUEST

To request further information about the employers featured in *The Times Top 100 Graduate Employers* and enter our free prize draw to win a **Ford Ka**, just complete your details below and return this postcard. Your information will be despatched to you directly from the employers.

NAME _____

UNIVERSITY _____

COURSE _____

TERMTIME ADDRESS

_____

_____

_____

EMAIL _____

❏ PRE-FINAL YEAR

❏ FINAL YEAR

Please tick the sectors that you are most interested in:

ACCOUNTANCY . . . . ❏
CONSULTANCY . . . . ❏
ENGINEERING . . . . ❏
FINANCE . . . . ❏
GENERAL MANAGEMENT . . . ❏
HUMAN RESOURCES . . . . . . ❏
INVESTMENT BANKING . . . . . ❏
IT . . . . ❏
LAW . . . . ❏
MARKETING . . . . ❏
MEDIA . . . . ❏
PURCHASING . . . . ❏
RESEARCH & DEVELOPMENT . ❏
RETAILING . . . . ❏
SALES . . . . ❏
OTHER . . . . ❏

Please tick the organisations for which you would like a graduate brochure and an application form:

ANDERSEN CONSULTING . . ❏
ARMY . . . . ❏
ARTHUR ANDERSEN . . . . . ❏
ASTRAZENECA . . . . ❏
BASS . . . . ❏
BNFL . . . . ❏
BRITISH AEROSPACE . . . . . ❏
BRITISH AIRWAYS . . . . . . ❏
BRITISH STEEL . . . . ❏
CHASE . . . . ❏
DERA . . . . ❏
DESG . . . . ❏
FORD . . . . ❏
GKN . . . . ❏
HSBC . . . . ❏
IBM . . . . ❏
ICI . . . . ❏
J.P. MORGAN . . . . ❏
KINGFISHER . . . . ❏
L'OREAL . . . . ❏

LLOYDS TSB . . . . ❏
LOGICA . . . . ❏
MCDONALDS . . . . ❏
MARKS & SPENCER . . . . . ❏
MARS . . . . ❏
MOTT MACDONALD . . . . . ❏
NESTLÉ . . . . ❏
NHS . . . . ❏
PFIZER . . . . ❏
PROCTER & GAMBLE . . . . ❏
PRICEWATERHOUSECOOPERS ❏
REUTERS . . . . ❏
ROLLS-ROYCE . . . . ❏
ROYAL NAVY . . . . ❏
SCHLUMBERGER . . . . ❏
SCHRODERS . . . . ❏
STANDARD LIFE . . . . ❏
UNILEVER . . . . ❏
UNITED BISCUITS . . . . . . ❏

The closing date to be included in the prize draw is 7th January 2000 but the Information Request service is available until 31st March 2000. If you do not wish to be included on our general mailing list and receive recruitment brochures and application forms from other relevant graduate employers, please tick here ❏

RESPONSE SERVICE
License No LON12390

1

High Fliers Publications Ltd
10A Belmont Street
LONDON
NW1 4YD

THE TIMES TOP 100 GRADUATE EMPLOYERS

Find out more about Britain's top graduate employers and you could start your career driving a brand new car!

INFORMATION REQUEST

To request further information about the employers featured in *The Times Top 100 Graduate Employers* and enter our free prize draw to win a **Ford Ka**, just complete your details below and post it back to - **High Fliers Publications Ltd, FREEPOST LON12390, London NW1 4YD**.

NAME _____

UNIVERSITY _____

COURSE _____

TERMTIME ADDRESS

_____

_____

_____

EMAIL _____

❏ *PRE-FINAL YEAR*

❏ *FINAL YEAR*

Tick the sectors that you are interested in:

ACCOUNTANCY . . . . ❏
CONSULTANCY . . . . ❏
ENGINEERING . . . . ❏
FINANCE . . . . ❏
GENERAL MANAGEMENT . . . . . . ❏
HUMAN RESOURCES . . . . ❏
INVESTMENT BANKING . . . . ❏
IT . . . . ❏
LAW . . . . ❏
MARKETING . . . . ❏
MEDIA . . . . ❏
PURCHASING . . . . ❏
RESEARCH & DEVELOPMENT . . . ❏
RETAILING . . . . ❏
SALES . . . . ❏
OTHER . . . . ❏

Tick the companies that you would like more information on:

ANDERSEN CONSULTING . ❏	LLOYDS TSB . . . . ❏
ARMY . . . . ❏	LOGICA . . . . ❏
ARTHUR ANDERSEN . . . . . ❏	MCDONALDS . . . . ❏
ASTRAZENECA . . . . ❏	MARKS & SPENCER . . . . . ❏
BASS . . . . ❏	MARS . . . . ❏
BNFL . . . . ❏	MOTT MACDONALD . . . . . ❏
BRITISH AEROSPACE . . . . ❏	NESTLÉ . . . . ❏
BRITISH AIRWAYS . . . . . . ❏	NHS . . . . ❏
BRITISH STEEL . . . . ❏	PFIZER . . . . ❏
CHASE . . . . ❏	PROCTER & GAMBLE . . . . ❏
DERA . . . . ❏	PRICEWATERHOUSECOOPERS ❏
DESG . . . . ❏	REUTERS . . . . ❏
FORD . . . . ❏	ROLLS-ROYCE . . . . ❏
GKN . . . . ❏	ROYAL NAVY . . . . ❏
HSBC . . . . ❏	SCHLUMBERGER . . . . ❏
IBM . . . . ❏	SCHRODERS . . . . ❏
ICI . . . . ❏	STANDARD LIFE . . . . ❏
J.P. MORGAN . . . . ❏	UNILEVER . . . . ❏
KINGFISHER . . . . ❏	UNITED BISCUITS . . . . . . ❏
L'OREAL . . . . ❏	

The closing date to be included in the prize draw is 7th January 2000 but the Information Request service is available until 31st March 2000.

Successful Job Hunting

by **Peter Johnston**
Vice President of the Association of Graduate Recruiters

Sooner or later your time at university comes to an end and the real world beckons. Deciding what to do and preparing for your first job is a major challenge, so where do you begin?

Whether you're planning a high-flying career, hoping to take time off for travel, or opting for further studies before beginning work, start by visiting your local university careers service. It provides the most plentiful amount of quality guidance, both in written form and in person from qualified careers advisers. Deciding what type of career to pursue can be an extremely hard decision but most people do have some idea about the kind of work they would like to do. Influences from your school, your family, your time at university, and any vacation experience that you've had all colour your views of possible employment and are important influences. Your careers service can help you understand your own priorities and set you thinking about the direction that is right for you.

The first real stage of job hunting is to read up about potential employers and the careers they offer. You can do this via the internet or use the huge numbers of publications that cascade from the careers service shelves each autumn. Get the basic facts and figures first - find out which companies recruit graduates into the areas that you are interested in and then read up about what these organisations do. Most employers produce lavish recruitment brochures which can give you this information along with case-studies of how recent graduates have fared in the early years of their career. Once you have read-up on a selection of employers you should have a clearer idea about those that appeal to you, and perhaps also begin to rule out those organisations that you wouldn't want to work for.

The next step is to add to these broad impressions of recruiters and actually meet the employers face-to-face. It is very important to actually relate to the type of people that you could be working with in the future.

There are two main chances to do this at your university and the first is at a campus careers fair. Many UK universities host a major fair during the early part of the autumn where a selection of employers large and small take part in a one or two-day event. These fairs are a very good way to see who is recruiting and often fifty or even a hundred different organisations attend such events.

Watch out from the start of your final year for the date of your local fair and on the day, the key advice is go along as early as you can. Employers' brochures tend to disappear very quickly and their representatives are certainly fresher in the morning than they are last thing in the afternoon. If there isn't a local fair being held at your university then there are a few regional events held in Birmingham,

Manchester, Glasgow and London where you can usually meet a wide selection of employers, although it may mean taking a day away from university to attend them.

So the autumn careers fairs are an excellent way to assess the recruitment market but it is unlikely that you'll be able to spend more than a few minutes with the employers that interest you. If you really want to test out their qualities then you'll need to go along to their autumn presentations. These special recruitment events are specific to the individual organisation that is hosting them and they give you up to two or three hours with the employer. Most presentations take place during the evening and many include some form of refreshment. The content of these events does vary but many feature a formal part to the presentation, with a question and answer session, followed by informal discussion.

The more enlightened employers adopt a more participative style which can give you a much better insight into their organisation, including activities such as interactive exercises which demonstrate the challenges of their business or skills training sessions. It is important to use these events to the full - talk to the recent graduates from the company who are present to find out how they are really getting on, speak to the recruiters and try to establish whether you could imagine working in the organisation. Be aware that employers do use these events to identify impressive students - notes are taken and followed up when applications arrive - so don't limit your chances by dressing inappropriately or by overindulging in the company's hospitality.

The number of presentations held at individual universities does vary considerably from over a hundred employers at certain institutions to just two or three events per week elsewhere. Make sure that you collect the programme of events from your careers service at the start of the autumn and keep in touch with them for details of last minute events or changes. Some employers operate a 'sign-up' procedure where you let the careers service know in advance the events you plan to attend. Be choosy about the presentations you go to and certainly don't try and see more than ten or twelve employers, or else you'll have no time for anything else.

There are several other alternatives to presentations which can help you experience a company at first hand. A few employers offer

STAGE 1 - INFORMATION GATHERING

There are a great many different publications and on-line sites that you can use to gather information about employers and their graduate recruitment programmes. Most are available from the university careers services but there are plenty of other sources as well:

- Almost every major employer has its own website and there are a host of commercial recruitment sites on the internet

- Make sure that you're registered with your careers service to receive their regular newsletters, bulletins & events lists

- Many employers promote their campus events in the main student newspapers, so make sure you get your copy

- Several national daily newspapers have weekly graduate jobs pages, look out for the 'Graduate Careers' section in *The Times* every Monday

"This is going to take a while . . ."

There are two main opportunities to meet with employers on-campus during your final year at university. The autumn careers fairs bring together large numbers of organisations for a single event, whilst many employers opt to hold their own individual presentations.

- Find out from the careers service when your local careers fair is taking place

- Get there early and spend time talking to the employers - don't just grab their brochures!

- Aim to attend a selection of employer presentations, but you won't have time to see everyone

- Try and dress smartly and make a point of speaking to the recent graduates at the event

- Be objective when you are comparing companies and remember that how you feel is important

"Where else will we get a free three-course meal at this time of night . . ."

places on Christmas courses - a two or three day event held for a limited number of final year students who participate in a lively programme of presentations, training exercises and business activities. The two main student careers organisations - AIESEC and the Student Industrial Society - also run a host of employer experiences, including company visits, skills sessions, and competitions.

Once you've seen employers in action and decided who to 'short list', the next stage is to make your applications. One of the most important things to establish straight away is when is the deadline. Every organisation operates to different timetables - some accept applications all the year round, others have a single deadline. Make careful notes of these details because you will shoot yourself in the foot if your application arrives a week late. Generally though, the earlier you apply, the better and certainly aim to get as many completed as you can before Christmas.

Employers like to receive their own forms, rather than the 'standard application form' which is available, unless they specifically state

otherwise. Their forms are widely available from careers services, via the internet or from employers direct. Before you start filling in the forms, do your homework. Understand why you want to apply for which organisations. One of the simplest questions that you will be asked at interview stage is 'why did you apply to us' and the information you provide on the application form will back up your answers. Time and time again, employers find that applicants don't have a plausible reason and they are the first people to be rejected.

All employers expect to receive a professionally-completed form from literate candidates. If you can't spell or are unable to write presentably then you are seriously limiting your chances. When an employer has a hundred applications to sift through for each graduate position, the easiest way to do a first sift is to go through and throw out the forms that are messy or are covered in corrections. Don't do yourself the injustice of making a poor first impression. On a practical level, if you make a mistake when you are completing a form, don't cross things out - get another form and start again. First

STAGE 3 - MAKING YOUR APPLICATION

Getting your application right is a big step towards success with an employer. The first impression you make and the information you supply will be key influences when the organisation decides whether to invite you to interview.

- Make sure you know when the application deadline is - it's no good applying two weeks late

- Take note of how the employer wants you to apply - is it using their form or with a CV and covering letter

- When you are filling in the form, if you make a mistake, start again - first impressions count

- Be truthful on the application form - if you bend the truth, you will be found out during the interview

- Don't leave large blank spaces on your form - every question needs to be answered

"I'm not sure that shop lifting counts as work experience."

impressions really do count.

The information that you are asked to provide on forms can be divided into two basic categories - factual information about your education, your interests and the work experience you've had so far; and longer, more searching questions which are individual to the company that you are applying to.

The golden rule about all your answers is don't lie and don't embellish your accomplishments, because competent interviewers will see through elaborations. Don't be 'Captain' when you were only 'Vice Captain', don't exaggerate your grades at GCSE or A-levels, and certainly don't overstate your likely degree result. Be honest but don't be afraid of putting down the most humble work experience that you've had - it all helps. Employers are looking for examples of when you've shown some real initiative and had experience of surviving in the working world.

Make sure you never leave sections on the application form blank - there's always something you can put in each section, but you don't necessarily need to fill all the space available.

The longer questions are not designed to catch you out and in many cases are not used to determine whether you are selected for first interview, but they are likely to be one of the main discussion points at the interview.

There is no right or wrong answer to the number of applications you should fill in. Twenty is probably the maximum that you'll ever have time to do, but most people are content with between ten and fifteen. If you are very certain that you know who you want to work for and are confident about the applications you are making, you may be able to apply to fewer organisations.

If your applications are successful, then the final stage of the job hunting process is the selection round, beginning with an interview. These can take place on campus or at a regional centre, or even at the employer's national offices. Early interviews are scheduled for before Christmas but the majority take place in January or February. If the date that you are given for interview interferes with your academic work, do not hesitate to explain politely to the employer that you are unable to meet the date they have suggested. Most will try to be flexible and accommodate you with an alternative.

Your first interview may be a nerve-wracking affair, but you will become more accomplished the more that you do. The purpose of the interview is to flesh out the application form, to test out the personal details that you have provided, and explore whether you have the interpersonal skills and the real motivation to be successful. The majority of interviews are conducted as one-to-one meetings and a good interview should enable you to respond to open questions, leaving you to talk for 80% of the time. It is very important that you know your application form. If you have included something on your form which is less than truthful then a professional interviewer will detect the look of surprise when you are confronted about it - a certain end to your application.

The next round of selection is commonly an assessment centre. This is effectively a second interview which involves an overnight stay - a combination of social activities and a range of exercises. These enable you to demonstrate your team working skills, your basic analytical and conceptual leadership abilities, and your future potential. Many companies now use a variety of aptitude tests to ensure that arts graduates are numerate and that technical graduates are literate.

Be aware that all of these elements of contribute to your final assessment, including the social element where you are interacting with recent graduates or other company representatives. The purpose of the event is to assess you as a whole person and if you are applying for a specific function you have to show there is more to you than just an interest in that area. Employers don't just want academic ability - you have to have management skill potential and strong communication skills.

If you're apprehensive about assessment centres then most university careers services keep files on previous students' experiences, and these can be a very useful way of preparing for them. The best advice is always to be yourself but it certainly helps if you have an idea what to expect.

After the centres you should hear very quickly whether you are to be offered a graduate job or not. If you are in the happy position of receiving several offers then don't automatically accept the highest salary package. Money is important but it cannot make up for working in

STAGE 4 - SURVIVING THE SELECTION PROCESS

Once your application has been accepted, you'll be invited for a first interview and then perhaps a final round assessment centre. Preparing for these selection activities will improve your chances of impressing your first employer.

- Your first interviews will probably take place on campus - if the dates you are given clash with exams or revision, then ask for alternative arrangements

- Keep a copy of each application form you fill in and re-read them before you go along to the interview

- Check the employer files at the careers service to see whether there is information about past assessment events

- Be aware that you will be assessed throughout your time with a company, even when you are socialising

"I got the impression the job was in the bag ..."

an environment that you are not comfortable with or in a career that you do not feel is right for you.

Weigh up how employers have treated you during the selection process and reflect on your impressions of the people you have met. You will probably know instinctively whether an organisation is right for you. Be wary of employers who try to force you to decide about their offer very quickly - this is too big a decision to rush.

What if it all goes wrong and your applications don't lead to interviews and offers? Well, the recruitment round is now spread over a much longer period and many employers take on a significant number of graduates during the summer. You'll probably find that your self confidence improves the second time around as you become better at filling in applications and performing at interviews. You can improve your chances by talking to others who have secured a job - what is it that they did differently? Consult the careers service and perhaps have a sample application form checked to make sure that you're not making major mistakes.

Whichever route you take to your first job will take considerable time and effort. You'll need to devote plenty of energy to the process but the reward is a first graduate job that can set you up for the career that follows.

It is an exciting time of change, and one that you can look forward to.

SUMMARY - THE RECRUITMENT TIMETABLE IN YOUR FINAL YEAR

- **October & November** - Careers fairs take place at universities across the UK and employers hold recruitment presentations.

  Watch out for certain employers, particularly investment banks, management consultancies, and companies holding Christmas courses who have very early application deadlines.

- **December** - The majority of employers with a single deadline require completed applications either just before or straight after Christmas.

- **January to March** - Employers invite students for first interviews and assessment centres. Most organisations try to make offers by Easter.

  Employers who recruit graduates round-the-year continue to accept applications from finalists.

- **June to August** - The summer recruitment round includes special careers fairs at certain universities and employers who still have vacancies conduct interviews and assessments until their places are filled.

"You can but dream . . ."

Making the most of University Careers Services

by **John Simpson**
Director of Careers Service at Imperial College, London

There is one part of every university that all students should make use of before graduating - the careers service. But what are they really for and how can they prepare you for life after your studies?

Careers services exist to help you find a graduate job, it's as simple as that. Large or small, each university in the UK provides a careers advisory service to help bridge the gap between academia and the working world. They are a central point of contact for employers seeking to recruit graduates and can offer you a convenient local source of guidance during your job search.

What they provide is information and advice. Information is the bedrock on which the services are founded and most have several hundred reference files about graduate employers, a library of careers literature, information files, videos, and guidance leaflets produced by the Association of Graduate Careers Advisory Services. Many also have computers which run the careers guidance system 'Prospects HE' and provide access to the internet.

Each careers service is staffed by a number of professional careers advisers, and information officers - experienced, skilled individuals with substantial knowledge of the job hunting process and employment.

So how should you use your careers service? The first step is to visit as early as possible, ideally during your first or second year, to begin investigating the resources that are available. Take time to explore your careers service and see all the information that is on offer. Talk to the information staff and understand the different sources of help that you can access.

One of the most common reactions for students just starting the search for a graduate job is 'Help, I don't what I want to do!' and whilst the careers library and other facilities may have plenty of detailed information about your options, the answer may be to use the Prospects HE computer system and then if needed, book an appointment with a careers adviser. This can be on a one-to-one basis or in a group but the aim is to help you understand the job hunting process.

Don't expect the adviser to give you a list of suitable employers or determine your direction for you. All careers services operate on a non-directive counselling principle, which means that whatever help and guidance they provide, the final decision about your career choices has to be made by you. Careers advisers are there to help equip you with the tools you need to make your decisions, to guide you to form action plans so that you can pursue your goals, and to give you the techniques that will enable you to adapt and develop your career in future.

A good careers adviser will ask you the questions that you need to ask yourself to discover what type of environment you are looking for, the kind of skills you can offer an employer, and

CAREERS SERVICES - FINDING THE HELP YOU NEED

The University Careers Services can provide you with practical guidance and assistance at each stage of your job search. Try and visit your careers service as early as you can to get to know the facilities they offer and the information that is available.

- **No idea of which career to consider?** Look at PROSPECT (HE) the computer-assisted guidance system
- **Want to speak to a careers adviser?** Book an appointment or check for the times when advisers run duty sessions
- **Need an employer brochure or application form?** Check in the careers library or speak to the information staff
- **Interested in attending a training session?** Look out for details of events in the term diary.
- **Want to go to an employer presentation?** Read the careers service newsletter and (if necessary) book your place as early as you can.

"We'd like nice jobs with big salaries and fast cars, please ..."

which career sectors you are most suited to for your graduate employment. They can't necessarily tell you whether one company is 'better' than another, or even whether they think you would do well at a particular organisation. You must do your own research and reach your own conclusions.

During the busiest times, usually during the autumn and after the first semester exams in January, access to careers advisers may be quite difficult. To see an adviser for a one-to-one consultation means that you will need to book a time and at these peak periods this can involve a wait of days or even weeks. If you are in a hurry, many services run a 'duty adviser scheme' where a single adviser is available for shorter 'across the counter' discussions on a regular basis. This is ideal if you just have a quick query, or need some very specific advice.

Once you are more certain about your direction, then the real process of job hunting begins. There's an enormous amount of information available via your careers service either on paper or from the internet, and directly from employers at their campus presentations or at careers fairs. The careers service often facilitates these events

and coordinates the different recruiters. Look out for the regular bulletins and newsletters that your careers service distributes to promote these activities. Check with your service to see whether you need to register to receive this information, or if it is delivered automatically to all finalists.

There are several specific skills which can make your job hunting more straightforward and successful, and the careers service can help you develop them. The first of these is producing your CV. Every employer puts communication skills right at the top of their list of requirements and that starts with making an effective application to them.

Although many companies prefer you to complete their own application form it is still extremely useful to have a really good CV that you can use as the basis for the forms that you are filling in. This means chronicling your education, work experience, achievements and extra-curricula interests - expressing yourself well, laying it out appealingly and making sure that the content is impressive. Rather than just saying that you've skills to offer, it means providing the evidence that you've actually got those skills.

the great **ford summer drive**

with power steering & driver's airbag

ka **£6,995**

with 1 years free insurance†

new v-registration available now

WHAT CAR?
**CAR
OF THE
YEAR
1999**
BEST CITY CAR

MILLENNIUM PRODUCTS

**for details of your nearest
ford dealer call 0345 55 22 77**

DEALERS

When you approach an individual application form, if these core details are covered in your CV you have done much of the hard work already.

Most university careers services run CV clinics which offer invaluable tips on the format, style and content that makes a good CV. Led by a careers adviser, these sessions are run for groups but offer individual attention at the end of the clinic. Many students are often just looking for reassurance that they are presenting themselves most effectively in their CVs, in their covering letters and in filling those large blank spaces on the application forms.

The other key stage that the careers service can assist with is the selection process, talking you through the interview process, describing what you can expect from employers and how to prepare for your first interview. Daunting as they may seem, interviews do become easier the more that you do.

Your careers service can also explain what goes on at assessment centres, the final stage in the selection process for many employers. These events often include exercises such as psychometric tests, numerical or verbal reasoning, and careers advisers are well-placed to prepare you for these experiences. There are plenty of helpful leaflets and AgCAS produce a number of videos on techniques for interview and selection events which are well worth watching.

Just how much time you spend using the careers service and its facilities is entirely up to you. If you feel that your degree course is leading you towards a specific career choice, then your time at the careers service is likely to be spent examining information about individual employers. If you are one of the many whose studies provide little clue as to what to do next, then you may find that you spend more time reading up on the many jobs that are available for graduates of 'any degree' background.

Outside of the careers service, the support that you receive from your university department for job hunting can vary enormously. It can be different from faculty to faculty even within the same institution, depending on the vocational nature of the degrees. Many universities though have a good network of academics and administrators from the different departments who come together to meet with the careers service or act as departmental careers advisers. They are a very good source of information within their departments if you want to follow a career within that particular subject.

But regardless of why and how you use the careers service or its facilities, the sooner you begin the process of job hunting, the more chance you have of finding the opportunity that is right for you. It is never too early to start thinking about the rest of your life.

CAREERS SERVICES - USEFUL PUBLICATIONS

There are literally hundreds of careers guides and other publications produced each year to help you find out more about possible career areas and individual employers. Many are these are stocked in the University Careers Services, either as reference copies or in bulk so that you can take copies away:

- **AgCAS leaflets** - These A5 size booklets provide excellent advice on a host of different career sectors, along with practical guidance on the job hunting process

- **Prospects** - This series of publications includes regular jobs bulletins such as *Prospects Finalist* and *Prospects Today* which are published with the latest vacancies during the year.

- **GTI Career Service Guides** - Several universities have glossy guides to their careers service which are packed with useful information & employer details.

"Just another 498 files to go ..."

the great **ford**
summer
drive

with power steering & driver's airbag

fiesta**finesse**
£7,995

with 1 years free insurance†

new v-registration available now

for details of your nearest
ford dealer call 0345 55 22 77

DEALERS

Don't graduate to the dole queue.

THE TIMES

TOP 100

GRADUATE EMPLOYERS

Andersen Consulting

Andersen Consulting is one of the world's leading management and technology consultancies. We work with some of the most dynamic organisations in the world who are seeking to explore new markets and lead their industries.

Andersen Consulting's mission is to help our clients create their future. We align ourselves with four competencies that must be involved in any project to deliver successful business change and work in cross-competency teams to deliver truly integrated solutions.

Success, for our clients and ourselves, means maintaining a high level of responsiveness and flexibility in order that continuous improvement becomes second nature. Our market focus enables us to be recognised by our clients as experts in their particular industries and to identify opportunities for innovative cross-industry applications.

To join, graduates should have a minimum of 22 UCAS points or equivalent and be expecting, or have, a 2:1 Hons degree or higher. While the degree discipline doesn't matter: personal achievement and commitment does.

Graduates should have an appreciation of business and an interest in information technology. While no prior IT experience is required, we do want graduates who are interested in learning about it. Our graduates need to be team players, outgoing and adaptable, and

with good communication skills. They must also be prepared to move around the UK and possibly abroad. Our firm is its people, which is why we invest a huge amount of time and money in the personal and professional growth of every one of them.

After a five week induction programme in London and Chicago, there are on-going opportunities to participate in prescribed and elective training courses and to attend competency and industry specific conferences. One key aspect that plays an important part in our people's development is utilising the global network of knowledge and experience available from colleagues around the world. To help with this, we have created 'Communities' - smaller groupings that provide accessible, supportive 'home bases' for everyone in the organisation.

Our sophisticated career development framework ensures accurate and timely performance feedback, on-the-job training, mentoring and career counselling. Andersen Consulting is a meritocracy in which performance and ambitions will determine how far an individual goes.

EMPLOYER FACTFILE

Total graduate vacancies   **350**

Functions that Andersen Consulting recruits for

CONSULTANCY	GENERAL MANAGEMENT
IT	HUMAN RESOURCES
FINANCE	

When to apply for graduate jobs

ROUND-THE-YEAR RECRUITMENT

There is no specific deadline for graduate applications, but applying early is strongly recommended.

Universities Andersen Consulting plans to visit during 1999-2000
Aston, Bath, Birmingham, Bristol, Cambridge, Cardiff, Durham, East Anglia, Edinburgh, Exeter, Glasgow Heriot-Watt, Lancaster, Leeds, Liverpool, London, Loughborough, Manchester, Newcastle, Nottingham, Oxford, Sheffield, Southampton, St Andrews, Strathclyde, UMIST, Warwick, York

Please check with your local university careers service for full details of events.

Finding out more information

BROCHURE HOTLINE - 0500 100189

COMPANY WEBSITE - www.ac.com

ADDRESS - Graduate Recruitment Manager, Andersen Consulting, 2 Arundel Street, London WC2R 3LT

Looking for a career that will suit you?
It's all about making an impact.

If you want a lively and challenging career that will fulfil your potential while keeping your options open, you should be talking to us about business and IT consulting.

Andersen Consulting can offer you an unparalleled range of innovative and flexible career opportunities. Imagine what you could accomplish at one of the world's leading management and technology consulting organisations.

Our clients recognise that Andersen Consulting offers the unique ability to align strategy with people, processes and technology - an approach that transforms visionary ideas into successful working realities. You'd team with some of the most successful organisations - those

seeking sustainable profound change, exploring new markets, leading their industries and creating their futures.

Andersen Consulting has an outstanding reputation for training and career development. We ensure that all our employees are equipped with the skills that provide the foundation of a fulfilling career, and in our meritocratic organisation, promotion is never very far away. You would join a community of professionals which has a particularly strong family spirit and provides constant support. Working at Andersen Consulting is all about teamwork and sharing of knowledge - developing relationships with colleagues and clients alike.

You won't have routine days at Andersen Consulting. You'll work in a dynamic, intellectually interesting environment, helping to make changes essential to a client's success. You will be able to make the most of your analytical skills, flexibility and resilience, working alongside like-minded and highly talented people.

Isn't this what you've been looking for in a career? To find out more about Andersen Consulting, please contact the Careers Service or call our recruiting helpline free on 0500 100189. You can also visit our Web site at www.ac.com

ARMY
BE THE BEST

The British Army consists of 110,000 men and women, tasked with providing a defence force for the UK and ready for deployment in international crises throughout the world.

The Army is manned by highly trained, efficient and motivated Officers and Soldiers - all with the most up-to-date technology and equipment.

To lead and manage this organisation, the Army is looking for young men and women of the highest calibre - people who have achieved significant success in their academic studies and in their extracurricular activities.

Whilst there are no 'typical' Officers, we need people who thrive on intellectual and physical challenge and who are able to demonstrate high levels of self-motivation, leadership, initiative and team-working skills. We will accept any degree discipline, although engineering and technical disciplines are especially welcomed.

Graduates start at the rank of Lieutenant with a highly competitive starting salary of £20,850 after training, with six weeks' annual leave.

Promotion is based on merit matched by substantial salary increases. Training begins at the Royal Academy of Sandhurst, where you will be taught basic soldiering skills and will be helped to develop leadership, interpersonal and managerial abilities.

Following 44 weeks at Sandhurst, you will enter your chosen specialist career area, and as your career progresses you will be given the chance to acquire both military and civilian academic qualifications, as well as receiving ongoing training throughout your career.

Engineers and those in the professional corps are encouraged to attain chartered status, and the opportunity exists to study for MA, MBA or MSc degrees and CIMA qualifications where applicable.

The Army recognises that retaining its position as one of the best armies in the world requires the best Officers and Soldiers in the world, and thus it places great emphasis on continuous training and career development.

Officers attend the Junior Command and Staff Course, and some are later selected to attend Staff College in preparation for increased responsibility and promotion to the highest ranks. The development of your career will be largely determined by your commitment and self-motivation.

The Army welcomes applications from eligible candidates no matter what their marital status, race, ethnic origin or religious beliefs.

The Army is committed to being an Equal Opportunities Employer and has a strict code of conduct covering racial, sexual discrimination and harassment.

EMPLOYER FACTFILE

Total graduate vacancies   **768**

Functions the Army recruits for
The Army recruits for graduates into the management of a range of specific areas including communications, logistics, engineering, welfare and administration.

When to apply for graduate jobs
ROUND-THE-YEAR RECRUITMENT

There is no specific deadline for graduate applications, but applying early is strongly recommended.

Universities the Army plan to visit during the 1999-2000 year
Aberdeen, Aberystwyth, Aston, Bangor, Bath, Belfast (Queen's), Birmingham, Bradford, Bristol, Cambridge, Cardiff, City, Dundee, Durham, East Anglia, Edinburgh, Essex, Exeter, Glasgow, Heriot-Watt, Hull, Keele, Kent, Lancaster, Leeds, Leicester, Liverpool, London, Loughborough, Manchester, Newcastle, Nottingham, Oxford, Oxford Brookes, Reading, Sheffield, Southampton, St Andrews, Stirling, Strathclyde, Surrey, Sussex, Swansea, UMIST, Warwick, York

Please check with your local university careers service for full details of events.

Finding out more information

BROCHURE HOTLINE - 0345 300111
(Quote reference TOE01)
COMPANY WEBSITE - www.army.mod.uk
ADDRESS - Freepost, The Army, CV37 9BR

COULD YOU COPE IF YOUR FIRST JOB WAS DIRECTOR OF A COMPANY?

It's a job working in one of Britain's most successful organisations.

Where you'll be part of a team of 120 highly motivated men and women. Where your management skills will be tested to the extreme every day.

Where the decisions you make aren't about saving company money, they're about saving company lives.

ARMY
BE THE BEST

For more information, send this coupon to: Freepost The Army, CV37 9BR, or telephone **0345 300 111** quoting ref **TOE02**.

SURNAME_____ MR/MS
BLOCK CAPITALS   PLEASE CIRCLE

FIRST NAME _____

ADDRESS _____

_____

POSTCODE _____ TEL (STD) _____ DATE OF BIRTH ____ / ____ / ____
The Army is committed to Equal Opportunities.   http://www.army.mod.uk

ARTHUR ANDERSEN

Arthur Andersen is a global professional services firm with four key service categories - Assurance & Business Advisory, Tax Consultancy, Global Corporate Finance and Business Consulting. Nothing surprising there, unless you thought we were simply boring, grey suited accountants, that is. More facts ... we employ over 61,000 people in over 260 offices around the world and our growth rate has consistently outstripped that of the competition.

We are the only professional services firm to operate a 'one-firm' concept - operating as a single partnership around the world, with everyone sharing the same values, standards and rewards. We work with all sorts of companies, from some of the world's biggest multinational companies to private owner-managed businesses and individuals. The resources and time we dedicate to this range of clients may differ, but our commitment to excellence does not.

We are looking for 650 outstanding graduates in any degree discipline to add value to our business throughout the UK. We have five cornerstones at the heart of our business strategy; increasing market share, achieving total client satisfaction, looking after our people, managing the quality and risk of our assignments and teaming. We want people who can help us achieve these objectives! Your views, your knowledge, your ideas, your personality, your style, your potential - these characteristics will colour our business and colour the way our clients see us and therefore are important to us.

You could join any of the four service categories mentioned above, and within these divisions there is also the possibility to train in specialist areas including actuarial consultancy, insolvency, technology and contract audit services. This means that you can have a career where you might help buy a company one day or clinch a multi-million pound deal the next. Maybe you'll introduce tailor-made business methodologies to world-leading companies or knock a few zeros off their tax bills.

Our commitment to education and training gives our people a competitive edge. Last year we spent over $300 million on training and development worldwide. You can expect to attend our international training courses at one of our training centres in Holland, Spain or the US, where you will develop your technical and non-technical skills.

You will also study for professional qualifications relevant to your chosen practice area, whether it is Chartered Accountancy, Chartered Institute of Taxation, or exams set by associations such as the Institute of Actuaries, the Institute of Personnel and Development or the Association of Corporate Treasurers. We will pull out all the stops to help you pass the exams. In addition, we offer all our staff the opportunity to study for a fully-funded MBA.

EMPLOYER FACTFILE

Total graduate vacancies   **650**

Functions that Arthur Andersen recruit graduates for

ACCOUNTANCY	FINANCE
CONSULTANCY	HUMAN RESOURCES
IT	

When to apply for graduate jobs

ROUND-THE-YEAR RECRUITMENT

There is no specific deadline for graduate applications, but applying early is strongly recommended.

Universities Arthur Andersen plan to visit during 1999-2000

Aston, Bath, Birmingham, Bristol, Cambridge, Cardiff, Durham, Edinburgh, Exeter, Glasgow, Heriot-Watt, Hull, Lancaster, Leeds, Liverpool, London, Loughborough, Manchester, Newcastle, Nottingham, Oxford, Reading, Sheffield, Southampton, St Andrews, Strathclyde, Swansea, UMIST, Warwick

Please check with your local university careers service for full details of events.

Finding out more information

BROCHURE HOTLINE - 0500 592800

COMPANY WEBSITE - www.arthurandersen.com

ADDRESS - Director of Recruiting, Arthur Andersen, 1 Surrey Street, London WC2R 2PS

AstraZeneca

AstraZeneca researches, develops, manufactures and markets pharmaceutical and agrochemical products to improve human health and nutrition worldwide.

Formed in April 1999 through the merger of Astra AB and Zeneca Group PLC, we are one of the world's top five ethical pharmaceutical companies, and the third largest supplier of agrochemicals.

We operate in some of the most competitive and rapidly evolving industrial sectors and offer graduates interesting and challenging careers. We aim to be the best in our chosen areas of business and to be so, we must continue to recruit the best.

Our product portfolio includes 'Losec', the world's leading pharmaceutical and 'Gramoxone', the world's second largest selling agrochemical.

We employ over 45,000 people worldwide. In research and development, we have over 10,000 people dedicated to the delivery of effective new products. Another 10,000 people are focused on making these products, applying their skills to ensuring our processes are among the best and most efficient. And our commercial strengths include a force of some 24,000 people in sales and marketing who promote and sell our products in over 100 countries.

We recruit graduates with First or 2:1 degrees - any subject, and PhD. We are looking for people with enthusiasm and drive who work well as part of a team and who will thrive in an environment where their skills, energy and commitment can make a real difference.

We want our people to achieve their best and aim to give them the right combination of freedom and support so that they can develop their potential to the full and channel their energy effectively to meet the challenges of working in a global business.

We offer each of our graduate recruits a personal development plan tailored to individual skills and aspirations, and an effective induction and management support on entry and throughout their career. Many departments use a 'mentoring' system.

Our graduate trainees have a real job from day one with guidance, supervision and coaching. Cross-functional moves are encouraged to help develop individuals. There may be opportunities to work abroad as part of your career development.

We offer a competitive starting salary and benefits package, and salary progression depends largely on your individual contribution.

creativity
through knowledge

In April 1999, Astra AB and Zeneca Group PLC merged to form AstraZeneca PLC.

Active in over 100 countries, AstraZeneca is one of the world's leading companies with a strong research base and the market presence to provide a powerful range of products designed to improve human health and nutrition worldwide.

Our business success depends on transforming knowledge and ideas into innovative products and services, and this can only be achieved through the intelligence, commitment and energy of our people.

If you would like to know more about us and the opportunities available to graduates within AstraZeneca, contact your local careers service or call 0171 626 3816 for a brochure.

www.astrazeneca.com

▲Bass

B ass plc is now a £4.6 billion operation and a major force in the global leisure industry. We operate in three core interrelated areas-hotels, leisure retailing and branded drinks.

Bass has been committed to the international hotel business since our 1988 acquisition of Holiday Inn International. This year we will welcome more than 150 million guests in over 90 countries to our hotels which now include the Crown Plaza and Inter-Continental chains.

Bass Leisure Retail's operations illustrate perfectly our ongoing commitment to offer our customers a diversity of great leisure experiences. Each of our brand names provide their own distinctive feel from All Bar One, O'Neill's, Edwards, Browns, Bar Coast and Harvester to the more traditional Taverns and Community Pubs.

Our branded drinks operations produce, market and distribute a strong portfolio of brands. Bass Brewers produce nearly 50 different brands including Carling, Caffrey's, Worthington's, Tennent's and Grolsch. Britvic Soft Drinks has its own bestselling brands such as Robinsons and Tango. Add to the list Pepsi and 7Up in the UK, and the scale and strength of our portfolio becomes evident.

The leisure industry is competitive, dynamic and innovative. The graduates we recruit possess the same qualities. We look for energy, vision and fresh thinking. Our graduates need astute commercial minds for a very demanding international arena because our industry demands that we are able to anticipate, innovate and turn change to our advantage.

At Bass we have a strong commitment to organic growth. We invest in our people and the Bass Graduate Programme is designed to produce our senior managers of tomorrow. The first two years' training is a combination of business skills and on-the-job development with professional qualifications where relevant. From the start of a career our graduates are given a real job to do, there are regular performance reviews and a mentor is chosen to provide guidance and support. We will require a minimum of 18 UCAS points and at least a 2:2 degree in any discipline.

What makes a great Experience?

The Bass Graduate Programme

Working at Bass is about creating great customer experiences. Our business can be fun and exciting but it also demands an astute, practical, commercial mind. Can you meet the challenge? Could you be one of the people making it happen at Bass? Would the Bass Graduate Programme bring out the best in you? For more details of graduate opportunities go to our website **http://www.bass.com/graduate** or call us on our recruitment line **0845 607 07 87** (calls are charged at a local rate)

B NFL is at the forefront of a rapidly changing, high profile nuclear industry.

We are leaders and our expertise spans across the whole range of the nuclear fuel business.

In an increasingly competitive international nuclear market our impressive track record gives us a significant competitive advantage.

We have worked hard to develop our international business, particularly in markets where nuclear power is expanding to meet the energy needs of industrialisation. In the US, we are the leading waste clean-up and decommissioning company.

Export customers already account for more than a third of our sales, and our ability to deliver proven solutions to the problems facing our customers overseas has helped to make BNFL one of the UK's top export earners.

The worldwide success we enjoy in our core market is underpinned by our commitment to technological leadership and we are now developing and applying many of our advanced techniques and processes for customers in related industries.

The safety and welfare of all BNFL employees, the general public and protection of the environment are paramount in all of BNFL's operations. Considerable resources are devoted to achieving and maintaining high radiological and conventional safety standards.

BNFL's ability to grow in the 21st century depends on the strength of our technology and quality of our people. We are commited to recruiting and developing a high calibre workforce.

Applicants should have or expect to achieve a minimum 2:2 degree (although a 2.1 or above is preferable) in a relevant subject, ie Chemical, Mechanical, Electrical, Control, Instrumentation and Civil Engineering. Chemistry, Physics, Health Physics and Safety and Mathematics. We also have a small number of Business and Commercial vacancies.

Our development programme combines technical and management training. You will be placed in a 'real' job from day one with real responsibility and challenges.

Our scheme is accredited by the IMechE, IChemE, RSC, IEE, IOM (pending), ICE and is supported by the IOP. We offer you unrivalled training and development opportunities and the chance to work in a company at the forefront of nuclear technology.

You will be assigned a personal mentor, providing support for accreditation, this can be supplemented by secondments outside your base department. Graduates are our future business leaders and this is recognised in the quality of our training and development programme.

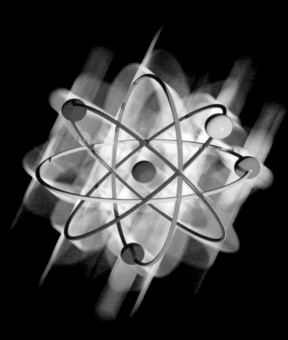

BNFL is at the forefront of a rapidly changing, high profile nuclear industry. We are leaders with expertise across the whole range of the nuclear fuel business and have offices in Britain, China, Japan and throughout Europe and the USA.

BNFL is a truly international company. Continual investment in research and technology has put us into the top 40 UK companies, made us a multi-million pound export earner and has enabled us to offer a complete range of nuclear expertise from fuel manufacture and waste management to transport, recycling and electricity generation.

To ensure the continuation of our success well into the next century, we're now looking for talented graduates to join us in all areas of the company. In particular, we have opportunities for the following disciplines:

- **Engineering (Mechanical, Electrical, Chemical, Control, Instrumentation and Civil)**

- **Science (Chemistry, Physics, Mathematics, Health Physics & Safety)**

- **Business**

Our development programme combines technical and management training. You will be placed in a 'real' job from day one with genuine responsibility and challenges. Our scheme is accredited by the Institute of Mechanical Engineers, the Institute of Chemical Engineers, the Royal Society of Chemistry, the Institute of Electrical Engineers, the Institute of Materials (pending), the Institute of Civil Engineers and is supported by the Institute of Physics. We offer you unrivalled training and development opportunities and the chance to work in a company at the forefront of nuclear technology.

You will be assigned a personal mentor and support for professional membership, this can be supplemented by secondments outside your base department. Graduates are our future business leaders and this is recognised in the quality of our training and development programme.

We currently have graduate opportunities to work at our sites based in West Cumbria, North West, South East and South West England.

You'll have, or be expecting to gain at least 2:2 in your degree, although a 2:1 or above is preferable, as well as having skills in communication, teamworking, problem solving and team leadership.

To prove our commitment to your career development, we're offering a generous benefits package, which includes a generous holiday entitlement and contributory pension scheme.

For further information and an application pack, telephone our Graduate Recruitment Hotline on 019467 86044.

Closing date for applications is 31 December 1999.

Visit our web site at www.bnfl.com

INVESTOR IN PEOPLE

BRITISH AEROSPACE

British Aerospace is a global aerospace and defence systems company, employing around 46,000 people. We are one of the UK's biggest exporters, with annual sales of around £8.6 billion, of which nearly 90% are exports. Working from sites across the country and the world, we create and apply the latest technologies through our engineering, and offer a wide variety of challenging and fulfilling careers in commercial and military aircraft, systems integration and management functions.

We are looking for talented and committed graduates to help us develop and deliver total solutions for customers on land, at sea, and in the air. Whether designing the world's largest airliner or the smallest of gyroscopes, or making complex systems work, every project will stretch you.

Our graduates work in engineering (including software and systems engineering), project management, manufacturing, finance, commercial, purchasing and human resources. For engineering positions, you should have at least 18 UCAS points and have, or expect a 2.2 honours degree or above, in any engineering or numerate subject. For non-engineering roles, you should have at least 22 UCAS points and have or expect a minimum 2.1 honours degrees or above, preferably in a business-related subject.

We have two entry routes for graduates, our Graduate Development Programme and SIGMA, our fast-track engineering management scheme. By joining the Graduate Development Programme, you gain real experience from the start by joining one of our business units. You will take part in a structured series of activities which build into an integrated programme for your personal and professional development, run in partnership with Lancaster University's Management School. As well as focusing on your professional specialsm, the programme will promote your key personal skills including teamworking, leadership, innovation and creativity.

If you are expecting a 1st or 2.1 and are interested in a career in engineering management, SIGMA can give you rapid career progression. This five year programme will give you real responsibility, practical leadership experience and professional qualifications in your chosen field. You will work in a variety of roles across our business units including international placements, and in partnership with some of the leading players in our industries.

Throughout your career with us, you will drive your development. You will regularly review your performance and agree the areas you would like to develop. You will have the chance to choose the experience, courses or materials from the diverse opportunities open to you across British Aerospace.

What do you want from your career?

Engineering Commercial Finance Human Resources Purchasing
Software and Systems Project Management Manufacturing

British Aerospace can give you all this, plus a head start in your career through:

- practical, real world experience as you face the technical and managerial challenges we deal with every day
- a structured Graduate Development Programme
- opportunities for placements to deepen and broaden your skills
- ongoing training in your function, usually leading to a recognised qualification
- a commitment to your personal development.

OPPORTUNITY   EXCITEMENT

if you have the vision, obey your ambition

We recruit all year round in regular cycles.
To be considered for the next round of interviews,
return your application form by the following dates:

Early deadline – mid November
Spring deadline – end April
Summer deadline – end July

For an application form contact

BRITISH AEROSPACE

Tel: +44 (0) 1252 384420 Fax: +44 (0) 1252 383465
http://www.baegrad.co.uk http://www.bae.co.uk

BRITISH AIRWAYS

At British Airways, we are determined to exceed customer expectations and provide the very best service possible for the 38 million people who fly with us every year.

Our goal is to be the undisputed leader in world travel and graduates have a vital role to play, bringing fresh ideas, new perspectives and even greater diversity to the workplace.

We recruit the following: Computer trainees, business analysts, business planning, general management, finance, pensions, purchasing, catering and engineering professionals.

All graduates must have or expect to gain an honours degree, class 2.1 or above, in any discipline. They are also required to have english and maths GCSE/O Level at grade C or above, and have the right to live and work in the UK (except General Managment). The engineering programme requires an engineering degree (excluding civil or chemical).

The graduate programmes vary in content and length but the core principles of development and having real responsibility from the start remain the same throughout.

Graduates at British Airways have a great start with a comprehensive induction, personal development plans, buddies and mentors. Some programmes require further study for professional development eg finance, purchasing, pensions.

EMPLOYER FACTFILE

Total graduate vacancies   **150**

Functions that British Airways recruit for

GENERAL MANAGEMENT	IT
ENGINEERING	PURCHASING
FINANCE	

There are also opportunities in Pensions, Catering, and Business Planning.

When to apply for graduate jobs

ROUND-THE-YEAR RECRUITMENT

There is no specific deadline for graduate applications, but applying early is strongly recommended.

Universities British Airways plan to visit during 1999-2000
Bath, Bristol, Cambridge, Cardiff, Durham, Edinburgh, Exeter, Glasgow, Leeds, London, Loughborough, Nottingham, Oxford, St Andrews, Sheffield, Warwick and York

Please check with your local university careers service for full details of events.

Finding out more information

BROCHURE HOTLINE - 01992 510507
COMPANY WEBSITE - www.britishairways.com
ADDRESS - British Airways plc, c/o Bernard Hodes Advertising (BHA), Salisbury House, Bluecoats, Hertford, SG14 1PU

Shape the route ahead.

At British Airways we have a highly developed sense of direction. A truly global company, we are a leader in the travel industry, reaching out to new destinations, developing new services, creating new ways of working. But the route we take towards our goals could soon be down to you. Graduates play a vital role in our business, bringing new skills and perspectives - and the potential to rise to the highest levels of management. In return we provide development opportunities that are second to none, with nine specialist professional programmes and a wealth of training and support. Is it time you plotted a course to British Airways?

BRITISH AIRWAYS
The world's favourite airline

www.britishairways.com

≡ British Steel

British Steel is one of Europe's largest steel producers and one of the UK's top 10 exporters with approximately 48,000 employees world-wide.

British Steel's consistent investment in research and development, high technology and award winning training has established our enviable position as one of the most successful British companies.

British Steel operate in over 70 countries world-wide and bring approximately £4 billion per year into the British economy. One of our recent initiatives is the single biggest capital investment since 1980's, amounting to £121 million for the whole project. By investing in methods to improve production British Steel are continually responding to the demands of our customers, ensuring our success for the future.

We offer graduate opportunities in Engineering, including Electrical/Electronic, Mechanical, Civil, Chemical, Environmental, Process Control, Metallurgy, Materials Science, Physics, Manufacturing/Production Management, Customer Technical Services, Commercial, Logistics, Supplies Management, Finance and Personnel. Entry is open to all graduates from a variety of backgrounds with a minimum 2:2 degree.

British Steel develop an individual training plan and provide a mentor for every graduate who joins us. Your training plan will encompass both residential courses and on-site training and include specialised technical, professional and management training.

British Steel encourage the attainment of professional qualifications and, where appropriate, provide support such as paid study leave or financial assistance.

We offer two distinct professional qualification programmes. The Accelerated Management Development Programme is for high potential young managers and may lead to an MBA awarded by Warwick University. The Doctorate of Engineering (EngD) programme provides a unique opportunity for graduates wishing to undertake doctorate research studies to gain a prestigious qualification, whilst gaining first-hand experience in industry. The programme is offered by British Steel, in conjunction with University of Wales (Swansea and Cardiff) and the Engineering and Physical Sciences Research Council (EPSRC).

Mentoring, often by a senior manager, provides guidance and career development counselling. Overseas secondment and exchanges are increasingly becoming an important part of management development.

We now only accept applications online through our website - please visit for further details of our graduate recruitment programme at www.britishsteelcareers.co.uk.

Most students want to travel the world. We're looking for people to conquer it.

hrough growth, vision and strength British Steel has become one of the most successful ompanies in the world. So It's not surprising that we look for similar qualities in our people. or more information on graduate recruitment, along with our on line application orm, visit our web site www.britishsteelcareers.co.uk

ritish Steel. Your World just got bigger.

CHASE

The Chase Manhattan Corporation is one of the largest bank holding companies in the US. With over US$361 billion in assets, operations in over 50 countries and clients in more than 200, its status as a global presence is indisputable.

Chase investment banking operations serve as an extensive client base of issuers and investors with a comprehensive range of capital-raising and advisory services.

We are recruiting graduates for our programme commencing September 2000.

Candidates who possess a drive for excellence are central to our future success. In return we offer you the best start to your career. We believe in recruiting the best graduates throughout Europe and strongly encourage those interested in Investment Banking to apply.

Chase takes its Graduate and Intern Development Programmes extremely seriously. Our Graduate Development Programme is regarded as amongst the best in the industry.

We develop our bankers' talent in a way that quickly makes them a contributing member of the team. Specifically, the programme combines 3-4 months classroom based training followed by placement and continuous development within each function.

The programme has been designed to be progressive and fully aligned to Chase's business needs.

To succeed through the programme, each graduate is required to be highly analytical, detail conscious and should be able to apply common sense and practical solutions to complex problems.

As you compare us with your other opportunities, keep in mind that Chase is acknowledged in the market-place for: a global wholesale client base that is second to none; an expertise in all the major industry sectors; a risk management culture that has allowed us not just to weather the market volatility of recent years, but to profit from it as well; a culture that is based on teamwork and the belief that Chase's future is primarily dependent on everyone working together across all product, industry and geographic groups to arrive at the best solutions for our clients; and a strong and well-managed balance sheet.

To take advantage of the opportunities Chase has to offer, you must be available to start work in September 2000. To apply, you need to complete our European Graduate application form. You can obtain this form from our website or from the Internet - www.gti.uk/employers.saf.htm. Alternatively, you can also obtain a hard copy in the post by calling our hotline.

50|50

This is the type of partnership we believe in at Chase – fifty fifty. An equal partnership of talented, creative people teamed with one of the world's largest and most successful Global Investment Banks.

Candidates who possess a drive for excellence offer us unlimited potential for success. In return, we offer you the best start to your career.

Our graduate training programme is considered one of the best in the banking world. The programme features superb training in Investment Banking, Global Markets (Capital Markets, Trading, Sales, Research) and IT. We pay excellent base salaries, banking benefits and performance related bonuses.

To learn more about the exceptional opportunities at Chase, telephone us on the Chase Graduate Recruitment hotline: 0171 382 9848; or visit our website at www.chase.com. Or, if you prefer, write to us at Graduate Recruitment, PO Box 11573, The Chase Manhattan Bank, London, E1 9FR.

GRADUATE CAREERS IN INVESTMENT BANKING
YOUR QUESTIONS ANSWERED

DERA

DERA, the Defence Evaluation and Research Agency, provides world-class scientific advice, innovative engineering solutions and a broad range of technical services to the Ministry of Defence (MOD) and industrial partners around the world.

We conduct research into air, sea and land systems, as well as into areas such as electronics, structural materials, command and information systems, weapons systems and chemical and biological defence. We also conduct trials for weapons and equipment, carry out investigations in support of explosives detection and ordnance disposal activities, and examine the physiological and psychological aspects of defence systems and military operations. On a more strategic level, we conduct operational evaluation studies, which underpin complex decisions of national importance.

We do not only focus on the defence of the realm, but also on the commercial transfer of military-driven research. From advanced air traffic systems to flat panel loudspeakers and carbon fibre, our expertise is benefiting the lives of people the world over.

DERA is the single largest employer of scientists in the UK. It's an exciting, challenging environment where change and evolution are the only constants. We are seeking analytically minded, innovative graduates from most science, engineering and numerate disci-

DERA Headquarters

plines for a mixture of permanent and fixed term appointments. We look for individuals with enquiring minds and a pioneering spirit - problem solvers who can use and develop changing technologies.

We provide high quality training programmes, individually designed to meet your requirements as well as those of the business. Supported by close mentoring, you can look forward to plenty of on-the-job instruction, together with substantial early responsibility on live projects.

Study towards further academic and professional qualifications (such as MSc, PhD or Diploma in Management Studies) is strongly encouraged and where appropriate, we will arrange for you to attend external courses or international conferences in your particular field. In fact, so long as you demonstrate commitment and potential, DERA will do all it can to help you realise your ambitions.

Think the unthinkable

and who knows where your ideas will lead?

Careers in

Research &

Development for

Science,

Engineering and

Numerate

Graduates

Inspiration is a mystery. No-one can tell when it will strike, or in what direction it will take us. That's why, here at DERA – the Defence Evaluation and Research Agency – we have developed a unique culture which encourages free thinking and actively promotes the pursuit of pure research. A culture which brings together the largest community of Scientists and Engineers in Europe and provides them with the ideal environment in which to push back the frontiers of knowledge.

If you want a future of inspirational research and development... if you want to think the unthinkable and turn it into reality, then phone our recruitment hotline. There's no telling where your ideas will take you. But, this could be your first step on a long and fascinating journey.

Phone our recruitment hotline for a brochure and application form: (023) 9233 5588 (24 hour answer phone).

www.dera.gov.uk/careers

DERA is an Agency of the MOD

DEFENCE ENGINEERING AND SCIENCE GROUP

The Defence Engineering and Science Group (DESG) is a community of over 17,000 professional engineers and scientists working in all areas of the Minstry of Defence (MOD) and its agencies.

Our skills include scientific research and development, operational analysis and assessment, procurement and project management, trials and evaluation and operational support to the Armed Forces. Our annual budget of £9 billion for equipment and systems procurement means the MOD is Britain's biggest single customer. We offer you the opportunity to work alongside some of the largest defence contractors in the UK and overseas. You'll be able to develop and practise commercial and business skills as well as your technical abilities.

We need people with an interest in defence who are technically competent, effective communicators; well organised; excellent negotiators; motivated and determined.

To join the Graduate Engineer Programme or the Graduate Scientist Programme, you will need to have the minimum of a second-class honours degree in a science or engineering discipline - electrical/electronic engineering, computer systems engineering, communication engineering, mechanical engineering, IT, mathematics, operational research, physics, psychology or statistical modelling.

To join the Fast Stream Development Programme, you should have, or expect to achieve this academic year, a minimum of a second-class honours degree in a science, engineering, mathematical or computing-related subject.

The Graduate Engineer Programme lasts up to two years, involving a number of work modules within the MOD and industry. Each placement lasts for three to four moths and is designed to satisfy the training requirements of the relevant engineering institution. After a further two years you should be able to apply for Chartered Engineer status with the relevant professional institution.

The Graduate Scientist Programme is designed to develop your scientific knowledge and skills to meet the needs of a specific post. It lasts for two years, during which you will be assigned to an MOD establishment to work on a scientific project. After satisfactory competion of your training, we promote you to Higher Scientific Officer (HSO) and move you into the post for which you have been trained. We help you do what it takes to become a chartered member of a relevant instituion.

The MOD Engineering and Science Fast Stream recruits highly able engineers and scientists who have the potential for accelerated promotion to senior positions. You'll be able to build a career that encompasses project management, research & development and policy making.

EMPLOYER FACTFILE

Total graduate vacancies   **80**

Functions that DESG recruit graduates for

ENGINEERING	IT
RESEARCH & DEVELOPMENT	

When to apply for graduate jobs

EARLY DEADLINE - NOVEMBER 1999

Five other deadlines also apply until July 2000 - check with your careers service.

Early applications are recommended as places for the assessment centre are filled on a first-come, first-served basis.

Deadlines for applications to the Fast Stream Development Programme are 17th September 1999 and 7th January 2000.

Universities DESG plan to visit during the 1999-2000 year
Bath, Bristol, Cambridge, Cardiff, Liverpool, Loughborough, Oxford, Sheffield
Please check with your local university careers service for full details of events.

Finding out more information

BROCHURE HOTLINE - 01225 449106

COMPANY WEBSITE - www.desg.mod.uk/

ADDRESS - Central MOD DESG Recruitment Office, PO Box 2443, Bath BA1 5XR

Help develop weapons of mass construction.

Graduate Engineer/Scientist Trainee Programme

Recent events have demonstrated the awesome power of modern weapons systems. But while conflict in the Balkans has grabbed the headlines, Britain's armed forces are fighting enemies who have been around for ever.

Famine still brings the threat of disease in its wake. Earthquakes will still reduce the lives of thousands to a struggle for survival, no matter how the world's political map changes.

More than ever before, Britain's armed forces are taking on age-old enemies like these. It may mean rebuilding bridges or restoring water supplies in hurricane-ravaged Honduras, or organising an airlift of food and medicines to refugees in the Sudan.

The post-Cold War world has brought new and unpredictable challenges to forces personnel: it's done the same to the engineers and scientists who create and supply the systems and equipment they need – the graduate engineers and scientists who work as civilians in the Defence Engineering and Science Group.

For them, it means designing for a wider range of operational scenarios than ever before, and for conditions ranging from frozen tundra to tropical rain forest. It puts an extra dimension on a career that's always had plenty going for it – training and development of legendary quality, opportunity to work with the latest management techniques as well as leading-edge technology.

It also offers you an unparalleled variety of roles as you carefully build your career. Together with everything else you'll be constructing.

If you're heading for or already have at least a second class honours degree in electrical, electronic, mechanical, systems or computer systems engineering, or naval architecture, get our latest graduate brochure from your careers office.

For a copy of our brochure, telephone 01225 449106 and quote TOP100, or write to: Central MoD Recruitment Office, PO Box 2443, Bath BA1 5XR, quoting reference TOP100.

DESG
DEFENCE ENGINEERING AND SCIENCE GROUP

www.desg.mod.uk/

There is something big going on at Ford Motor Company. A defining period in our history. A transformation to the world's leading consumer company that provides automotive products and services. It's an exciting shift in our philosophy. It's opening the door to truly astonishing careers. And is creating countless opportunities for you to make an impact.

To ensure the success of our transformation, we are looking for individuals who thrive on innovation, leadership and growth. People who are dedicated to our consumers, our communities and the environment. People who demonstrate respect, resourcefulness and passion...

Our Engineering graduates need either a BEng or MEng degree, with a minumum of a 2.1. For all other functions, any degree discipline is acceptable.

On joining the Company, you will embark on a training and development process, which includes the following key elements. The 'New Employee Orientation' is a formal induction programme for all gradautes. You will learn about all aspects of Ford's worldwide operations and the Company's future plans. You will meet and work with your peers, developing a network of contacts from a wide range of functions and disciplines.

The 'Professional Development Plan' is the ongoing training and devel-opment process. It includes training programmes for engineers which are fully accredited by the IMECHE and the IEE and a mentor is assigned who regularly reviews each individual's progress. Graduates in Finance and Human Resources are strongly encouraged to study for their respective CIMA and IPD exams.

The 'Graduate Development Programme' is a formal training course undertaken during the first 12-18 months of your career and is designed to enhance your personal and professional effectiveness and plan the next stages in your development.

Your 'Personal Development Plan' is the self-managed aspect of your training and development and Ford will support you with first-class facilities.

The 'Leadership Development Process' was launched to support the needs of the business and the development of future leaders in the Company. It is a jointly managed initiative which provides linkage between you, your supervisor and the appropriate Personnel Development Committee (PDC). You are provided with developmental opportunities to complement organisational succession plans and to maximise your contribution to the Company's business objectives.

Ford. For thought.

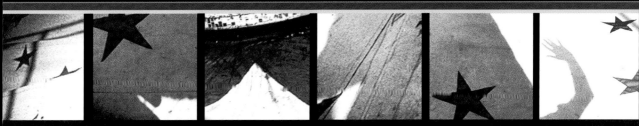

Graduate Careers 2000

Engineering	To find out more about Graduate Opportunities
Finance	visit our website www.ford.co.uk/recruitment
Human Resources	or write for information to: The Recruitment
Marketing, Sales & Service	Department, 15/9000, Ford Motor Company
Process Leadership	Limited, Dunton Engineering Centre, Laindon,
Purchasing	Basildon, Essex SS15 6EE.
Visteon-Commercial	
Ford Credit	

www.ford.co.uk/recruitment

GKN is a global industrial company that operates in more than 40 countries and employs over 54,000 people in its subsidiaries and joint ventures. 1998 was the fifth consecutive year for which the company reported record results with sales of £ 3.7 billion.

Its activities are focused on the automotive, aerospace and industrial service sectors and it has leadership positions in all of its major products and services. In automotive systems, GKN is a global first tier supplier to the world's manufacturers of cars, light commercial vehicles, trucks and off-highway vehicles.

We are the world's leading manufacturer and supplier of constant velocity joints and are also number one in the production and supply of powdered metal components. GKN Westland Helicopters is one of the world's leading helicopter prime contractors and GKN Westland Aerospace is rapidly emerging as a leading supplier to the world's aircraft and engine manufacturers.

GKN's vision is built on a commitment to growth and performance. It actively fosters an entrepreneurial culture across all of its businesses and its goal is to lead and excel in every market it serves.

We are looking for people who are highly motivated, enthusiastic and adaptable, and who learn fast. The essence of our approach is to create an intensive period of learning through a variety of short, challenging projects.

The projects are real jobs. So, we're looking for achievers, people who are determined to succeed, who are ready to take responsibility, want to get results and make a contribution. We want people with the potential to develop into leaders in our business - innovative, entrepreneurial, organised and able to work well with others.

The GKN Group Graduate Development Scheme provides individual programmes of learning and development, achieved through a sequence of 3 to 5 projects in different GKN businesses, across our aerospace and automotive divisions, including at least one overseas placement. We don't select for any one company or division in the Group or any particular job. We are confident that the people selected will take on leading roles in the organisation.

Language classes are provided in the first year, followed up with a placement in a country where you will need to use it. If you already have foreign language skills, we would want you to add to those with a new language. Some of the countries where GKN Group Graduates are currently working are Germany, France, Italy, Spain, Poland, Mexico, Thailand and the USA.

The scheme's supported self-managed development is principally through the experience gained on projects but this is supported by short courses in communication, project management and personal organisation and finance.

Think of the person that heads the team that uses the technology that produces the results that leads the industry.

THINK BIGGER. THINK GKN.

GKN PLC GRADUATE OPPORTUNITIES 2000.
FOR MORE DETAILS CALL 01527 533393 OR VISIT US AT WWW.GKNPLC.COM

HSBC

Headquartered in London, HSBC Holdings plc is one of the largest banking and financial services organisations in the world. The HSBC Group's international network comprises more than 5,000 offices in 79 countries and territories, operating in the Asia-Pacific region, Europe, the Americas, the Middle East and Africa.

With primary listings on the London and Hong Kong stock exchanges, shares in HSBC Holdings plc are held by some 170,000 shareholders in more than 90 countries and territories.

Through a global network linked by advanced technology, the Group provides a comprehensive range of financial services: personal, commercial, investment and private banking; trade services; cash management; treasury and capital markets services; insurance; consumer and business finance; pension and investment fund management; trustee services; and securities and custody services.

Graduates at HSBC join one of four programmes - commercial banking, information technology, international management, and investment banking & markets.

For commercial banking, we are looking for graduates with a minimum of a 2:2 classification in any discipline, who will enjoy making decisions, establishing relationships and helping our customers to 'sort money out'. Our graduate trainees receive a structured training programme which includes the opportunity to study for the Associateship of the Chartered Institute of Banking qualification which is linked to the award of a BSc (Hons) degree in Financial Services.

Within IT, we require graduates with a 2:2 or higher. Our trainee programme helps you become an IT professional, regardless of your degree discipline. Real project work, with real impact, is blended with classroom and on-the-job training to ensure you are fully equipped with the technical knowledge to develop an exciting career with this global company.

For the international management programme, we are looking for graduates from any discipline with a 2:1 degree. Following a residential programme in the UK, international managers join a development programme designed to ensure they will gain an understanding of the principles of financial services and international management. This training takes place in any country that the group operates in.

Graduates applying for positions in our investment banking and markets need a minimum of 24 UCAS points and a 2:1 degree, preferably in a numerical or business-related degree subject. After an intensive eight-week training programme which is comprehensive, practical and tailored to meet specific needs and roles, you will either go directly into the business area you have specifically chosen or join a rotational scheme for up to two years.

EMPLOYER FACTFILE

Total graduate vacancies   300

Functions that HSBC recruit graduates for

INVESTMENT BANKING	IT
FINANCE	

Opportunities are also available in International Management.

When to apply for graduate jobs

EARLY DEADLINE - 3rd DECEMBER 1999

This is the deadline for applications to the investment banking & markets and international management programmes.

Applications are accepted throughout the year for IT and other commercial banking positions.

Universities that the HSCB Group plans to visit during the 1999-2000 year
Bristol, Durham, Edinburgh, Exeter, Leeds, Manchester, Nottingham, Oxford, UMIST

Please check with your local university careers service for full details of presentations and careers fairs.

Finding out more information

COMPANY WEBSITE - www.hsbc.com/recruitment

BROCHURE HOTLINE -
Commercial Banking & IT: 0800 289529
Investment Banking & Markets and International Management: 0171 649 6103

ADDRESS -
Commercial Banking & IT: PO Box 1355, Sheffield S1 3SB
Investment Banking & Markets and International Management: 32 Aybrook Street, London W1M 3JL

Possibly the biggest hit with **graduates** this year.

Commercial Banking
Information Technology
International Management
Investment Banking and Markets

Unfolding Futures
www.hsbc.com/recruitment

YOUR WORLD OF FINANCIAL SERVICES

IBM is at the cutting edge of new technology and can offer recent graduates an unparalleled career in one of the fastest moving market places in the world.

We are the world's largest IT company competing in virtually every area of IT and operating in over 130 countries with approximately 291,000 employees. IBM provides products and services that improve customers' competitive positions - our outlook is focused firmly on the customer.

IBM is looking for intelligent, responsive and committed graduates who possess excellent problem solving skills and are good team players. To join us you will need a degree (with a minimum of 2:2) in an IT related or numerate subject such as Maths, Physics or Engineering. In addition we will consider candidates with excellent degree results in non-technical subjects. Your academic credentials must be supported by a real passion to apply technology in a business environment.

Graduate recruits typically follow a thorough programme of induction training to develop technical, business and personal skills. You will design a tailor made training package with your manager which will include technical and personal skills training specific to your job role.

You can specialise in areas such as Lotus Notes, Networking and Windows NT and there will be the opportunity to become a certified professional in your area of expertise.

IBM offers over 300 classroom courses, 200 self study courses and external MSc/MBAs etc.

$= mc^2$

What's
missing
from your
theory?

Graduates

e-business may not be central to Einstein's theory of relativity, but its implications are no less revolutionary. At IBM, we're designing and implementing e-business solutions that span entire industries and cover the globe.

If you're keen to apply your academic knowledge to a culture that's committed to changing the way people work, we'll help you make the difference at IBM.

The opportunities for Graduates are diverse. Our portfolio of services ranges from software development to technical support. Although we recruit Graduates from a wide variety of degree disciplines, a large number of our vacancies do require IT or numeric degrees. However, the 60% of Graduates who joined us in 1998 who did not have an IT related degree, found no shortage of challenges to stretch their talents.

The main qualities we are looking for are enthusiasm, good problem solving skills, team players and a passion for IT.

If you match these qualities, you'll find us equally responsive — which is the reason our recruitment process is year-round. So, even if you've taken time off to travel, or if it's your first job, we'll be happy to hear from you.

To apply, please phone 01705 564015 for an application form, speak to your Careers Adviser or apply on-line via our Website.

IBM is an equal opportunities employer.

Check out the IBM Website at: www.ibm.com/employment/uk

add **@** to your career

e-business

Solutions for a small planet

The ICI Group consists of a family of truly international businesses with a combined turnover of in excess of £9 billion. Working with our customers we use the creative application of science to create products which will enhance the quality of people's lives around the world.

From decorative paints with brands like Dulux and Cuprinol, to food ingredients, personal care products, speciality polymers, electronic materials, fragrances and flavours, ICI products stimulate the senses and impact all aspects of modern living.

ICI has evolved over the last few years to become one of the world's largest speciality products and paints companies with an impressive record of innovation and an ability to restructure itself to meet the needs of an increasingly global marketplace.

We recruit graduates from any degree discipline, but you must have a minimum two European languages including English. We offer you challenging work, early responsibility and varied global opportunities

alongside a competitive salary and benefits package.

Your development is of the utmost importance to ICI. You are our future leaders and senior business managers. Our European Graduate Development programme will ensure that you will receive the experience and training you need to go as far as you can.

Within all the ICI group businesses, the environment is vigorous. But then it is this environment, coupled with leading management, mentoring and personal development support that makes our people not only the world's best but some of the most significant shapers behind consumer markets of the future.

This is the essence of how ICI businesses work - people who recognise when to be leaders and when to be team players. It's rigorous and demanding, but if you have it in you, you can really enhance people's lives around the world with ICI.

A real job with real impact right from the beginning.

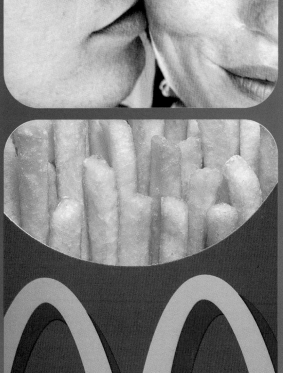

 enhancing people's lives

From exclusive ingredients for McDonalds to the vibrant array of Dulux paints, ICI develops specialty ingredients and products for some of the world's most successful brands. It is our expertise and innovation which helps shape tomorrow's markets in almost every aspect of modern living. Are you looking for an international management career for a world-class organisation which enhances people's lives on a global scale?

Find out how ICI can enhance your life today...

Tel: Freephone + 44 800 028 3376 ref 509

JPMorgan

J.P. Morgan is a global financial services leader transformed in scope and strength, with its roots in commercial, investment and merchant banking.

The firm, for over 150 years regarded as one of the world's strongest and most widely respected financial institutions, today offers sophisticated financial services to companies, governments, institutions and individuals. It advises on corporate strategy and structure; raises equity and debt capital; manages complex investment portfolios, and provides access to developed and emerging financial markets.

The firm employs about 15,000 members of staff in 33 different countries. In Europe, about 300 graduate recruits are employed each year.

J.P. Morgan recruits candidates from all degree disciplines for opportunities in four areas: Investment Banking, Markets, Asset Management Services and Business Infrastructure Management. As our standards are high, we look for evidence of academic excellence and outstanding personal achievements.

Successful candidates can expect early responsibility and accelerated progression in a meritocratic environment. The speed of your development is dictated by your abilities and motivation. Graduate trainees need to have a quick analytical mind, an ability to think broadly, a flair for conveying innovative solutions to problems and persuasive presentation and communication skills. Some disciplines require numeracy and the ability to work well in a team environment.

Morgan's graduate training programmes combine on-the-job learning with classroom instruction run to the same standard as the finest US business schools, with some courses based in New York. There are four programmes, each focusing on developing the knowledge, capabilities and skills needed for that area of business.

Business Infrastructure Management offers positions in two tracks: the Generalist programme prepares you for internal consulting assignments in a variety of groups, including Audit, Financial, Operations and Technology, and the Applications Delivery Programme prepares you to work in business-aligned technology teams.

The Investment Banking Programme is designed to prepare you to be an investment banking professional working in Advisory (M&A), Capital Markets or Equities.

On the Global Financial Markets Programme, you will learn how to value, trade and sell key financial products such as bonds, swaps, futures and options in the pressurised environment of the dealing room.

The Asset Management Services Programme programme prepares you to work in the Investment Management Group or the Private Client Group.

I believe in opening my own doors.

I believe a great firm has many doors.

I don't believe in following a career path.

I believe in building my own.

I believe my job is an investment.

I work for J.P. Morgan.

Morgan offers exciting and rewarding career opportunities in
Investment Banking, Markets, Asset Management Services,
and Business Infrastructure Management.

www.jpmorgan.com/careers

KING**ƒ**SHER

Kingfisher plc is one of the world's most successful multi-category retailers, concentrating on the home improvement, electrical and general merchandise sectors. Our brands extend throughout Europe, the Far East and South America. Kingfisher's vision is to double the size of the business within five years and our current status reflects our desire and potential to grow.

Kingfisher's link with Castorama, one of France's leading home improvement groups, through its merger with B&Q, has created Europe's leading home improvement retailers - more than twice the size of its nearest European rival.

With almost 700 stores in eight countries, Kingfisher Electrical, based in Paris, is a major force in European electrical retailing and a growing world player. Our brands include Darty, a leading electrical retailer in France, Comet in the UK, Vanden Borre in Belgium, BCC in the Netherlands, But in France, Electric City in Singapore and Promarkt in Germany.

Kingfisher has over 1500 general merchandise stores on Britain's high street, with many of its brands enjoying market leading positions; they include Woolworths, the family store, Superdrug, an important player in health and beauty, MVC the music and video store, and Entertainment UK, the leading distributor of entertainment products.

Expansion is set to continue within these sectors. However, growth and improvement will not happen successfully unless Kingfisher invests in the right people. The Group has therefore invested in the development of a new cadre of management.

The Kingfisher Management Development Scheme (KMDS) offers exceptional training and opportunities to able and ambitious graduates wishing to reach senior management within seven to ten years. Applicants to KMDS should have or expect to obtain a minimum 2:1 degree, and we accept applications from any discipline, although you should also have a minimum GCSE in a non-English language and good A-level grades.

Our graduate recruits start with an initial six month placement in retail, followed by at least two other business functions during the first two years, eg Marketing, Buying, Logistics, Distribution, Property, Management Information Systems, Finance and Human Resources. You will undertake skills training courses and study for an exclusive postgraduate qualification in Management Studies awarded by Templeton College, Oxford University, covering all aspects from supply chain management to international business strategy. We offer real responsibility through a structured, yet flexible scheme, with support mechanisms allowing you to achieve your career goals.

EMPLOYER FACTFILE

Total graduate vacancies   **50**

Functions Kingfisher recruit for

RETAILING	LOGISTICS
GENERAL MANAGEMENT	HUMAN RESOURCES
PURCHASING	IT
MARKETING	FINANCE

Opportunities are also available in Property.

When to apply for graduate jobs
EARLY DEADLINE - 14th JANUARY 2000

Universities Kingfisher plan to visit during the 1999-2000 year
Cambridge, Cardiff, Durham, Edinburgh, Exeter, Leeds, London, Manchester, Nottingham, Oxford, Warwick
Please check with your local university careers service for full details of events.

Finding out more information

KMDS graduating from Templeton College, Oxford University

BROCHURE HOTLINE - 0870 600 3377

COMPANY WEBSITE - www.kingfisher.co.uk

ADDRESS - 32 Aybrook Street, London W1M 3JL

KMDS

Kingfisher Management
Development Scheme

The direct route to senior management

KING*f*SHER

The KMDS?
It's the direct route to
senior management'

Tamara Gurajena, KMDS trainee

The Kingfisher Management
Development Scheme (KMDS)
aims to take top quality
graduates and develop them
into senior managers within
seven to ten years. If you'd like
to find out how, please call our
hotline number for a brochure
pack and application form:
0870 6003377

L'ORÉAL

L'Oreal is the world leader in the cosmetics market. With 300 subsidiaries operating in over 150 countries, L'Oreal is the most international of all major cosmetics groups. Brands such as Elvive, Fructis, Ambre Solaire, Lancome, Vichy, Redken, Ralph Lauren, Giorgio Armani and Maybelline are developed, manufactured, marketed and sold throughout the world.

L'Oreal recruits graduates from a wide range of university courses and backgrounds. The company does not have any specific requirements in terms of degree subjects, with the exception of those wishing to work in manufacturing who should have a relevant degree eg engineering or science. Excellent academic results are important, and a second language (not necessarily French) is advantageous but not essential.

Graduates join L'Oreal initially as Management Trainees and are provided with a tailored training programme. This lasts for 9-12 months and is based on active learning, in addition to formal training courses.

The modular training programme provides the opportunity to experience different areas of activity within the business. Each module offers real responsibility and Management Trainees are expected to make a tangible contribution to the business while increasing their skills and knowledge. Thereafter progression is typically rapid and may provide international experience.

L'Oreal International Teams

«A CAREER WITH

L'ORÉAL

BECAUSE YOU'RE WORTH IT...»

IF YOU VALUE...

- playing an active part in a thriving business within an international, unique and trend-setting environment,

- innovating and creating,

- being recognized and rewarded for your ideas, your actions... your talent.

...A CAREER WITH L'ORÉAL : IT'S WORTH IT.

We can offer you :

- cutting-edge research and the expertise of 90 year's success as the leader in beauty products,

- constant challenges in a fast-growing, unique global industry,

- continuous training and international exposure working on world-leading prestigious brands,

- exciting career opportunities worldwide and rapid responsibility, such as managing one of our 200 + business units in your early thirties,

- the chance to be part of a winning team of highly talented people, who together have achieved double digit profit growth for the last 15 years... with passion.

A career with L'ORÉAL, because you're worth it.

www.loreal.com

L'ORÉAL
WORLD LEADER IN BEAUTY PRODUCTS

Lloyds TSB

W̲e are a leading UK based Financial Services Group whose businesses provide a comprehensive range of banking and financial products and services in the UK and overseas. The launch of Lloyds TSB on June 28th created a new organisation with a distinct identity and personality. We wanted to launch a new bank for our 16 million customers that really suited their needs - and it signals a totally fresh approach to providing financial products and services.

We're looking for confident, motivated people who have a minimum of 18 UCAS points and who have gained, or are expecting to gain, a minimum of a 2:2 Honours degree (or ordinary degree from a Scottish University) in any discipline.

There are special requirements for some of our programmes - such as the International Banking programme where you need to be fluent in Spanish, Portuguese or a Latin-based language. For all our other programmes, we can only accept applications from those candidates who no not require a UK work permit. Please see our website for more detailed information.

Applications from people with disabilities and members of ethnic minorities would be particularly welcome, as these groups are currently underrepresented in our workforce.

Each of our Specialist Management Development programmes has 3 key elements. Firstly, you will work on a series of live projects in different departments, gaining hands-on experience and contributing to the success of the company from day one. Second, you will attend training sessions and workshops that will help you to gain a unique set of skills that will make you extremely marketable.

Our programmes also offer each trainee the opportunity to study for a relevant professional qualification, such as IPD, CIMA, DMS, CIM and FPC. We will pay for all your course material, exams and study leave. At the end of your training (usually lasting about 2 to 3 years) you will have all the skills and experience you need to secure a Managerial level position with us. The career opportunities with us are excellent. And the training and personal development will not stop when your training programme is over - we believe wholeheartedly in career-long learning.

Please apply to us using our employer application form. You will find versions of this on our website, which you can either download or complete online.

EMPLOYER FACTFILE

Total graduate vacancies   **120**

Functions Lloyds TSB recruit for

ACCOUNTANCY	FINANCE
MARKETING	HUMAN RESOURCES
RETAILING	

When to apply for graduate jobs

DEADLINES VARY - REFER TO WEBSITE

Universities Lloyds TSB plan to visit during the 1999-2000 year
Birmingham, Bristol, Edinburgh, Lancaster, Leeds, Liverpool, London, Loughborough, Manchester, Newcastle, Nottingham, Oxford, Reading, Sheffield, Southampton
Please check with your local university careers service for full details of events.

Finding out more information

BROCHURE HOTLINE - 07000 783955

COMPANY WEBSITE -
www.lloydstsbgraduate.co.uk

ADDRESS - c/o TMP Worldwide, PO Box 2784, London W1A 5JL

I want to become an *expert* in my *chosen* field

I want *training* to improve my career prospects

I want *responsibility* in a real *job*

how can
we help you
make it happen?

Whatever your aspirations, you can make them happen with one of the UK's largest financial services groups.

Our structured training programmes lead to professional qualifications across a wide variety of business areas, and you'll find no shortage of challenges helping to shape the future of our dynamic organisation.

For more information on what we can offer you, visit our website: **www.lloydstsbgraduate.co.uk**

Lloyds TSB
Your life. Your bank.

˥ogica

Our mission at Logica is to help leading organisations worldwide achieve their business objectives through the innovative use of information technology. We work for major blue chip organisations, on a global basis, on IT assignments which are critical to their future business success.

We are looking for honours graduates in computer sciences, engineering, mathematics, physics or any logical or numerate discipline. Computing experience is preferred.

During the first two years, following an intensive four-day induction module, our graduates attend a series of foundation modules called InLogica, which have been designed to develop skills in terms of business focus, client focus, interpersonal skills, self management and career focus.

For you to build your personal effectiveness and establish the foundations of a longer-term career within Logica, you will need the basic tools and processes valued by the business.

InSight Induction, which usually takes place during your first week, introduces you to the business, the way Logica works, and our core values. This is followed by InBusiness: after two or three months, you will spend three days investigating how and where Logica conducts its business, and the processes and methods we use. InProjects is a day course,

undertaken four to six months after you join, and will be spent looking at the way Logica runs projects for its clients. InTeams: after nine to 12 months, you will have a three-day session investigating teamworking at Logica.

In addition, each person will follow their own individual training plan and career path. Business needs may dictate that you supplement your foundation modules with other specific courses, for example technical training in particular computer languages or specific management skills development.

logica

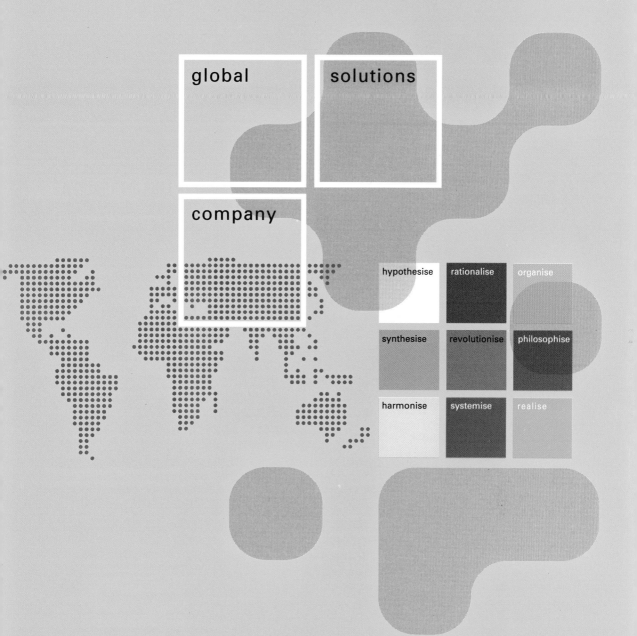

global

solutions

company

hypothesise	rationalise	organise
synthesise	revolutionise	philosophise
harmonise	systemise	realise

For a career in information technology contact:
The Graduate Recruitment Office
Logica
Freepost 21
London W1E 4JZ
Tel: 0171 446 2333
http://www.logica.com/jobs/uk/graduate/
email: graduaterecruitment-uk@logica.com

There are many factors behind the McDonald's success story, from our high-quality products to our exceptional standards of customer service. But our real strength is people - the individuals whose ability, initiative and attention to detail have made us the world's most popular quick-service restaurant.

We have over 24,000 restaurants in 113 countries, with plans to open 100 new restaurants in the UK every year until the year 2000. The result? One of the most challenging and potentlly rewarding career environments for gradautes.

As a successful graduate in any degree dicipline, you will have demonstrated your self-discipline, attention to detail, and ability to set and achieve worthwhile objectives. We value these qualities, they are essential to the success of any McDonald's manager. But we look for other qualities too. The ability to lead and motivate others, the initiative to explore new ideas, and the commitment to become completely involved in the day-to-day operation from the beginning. You also need the ability to assume a high level of responsibility early in your career. It is not unusual to be managing a restaurant within two to three years.

You'll be an effective people-manager, someone who can lead, persuade, guide and motivate staff to achieve consistent standards of business performance. Someone who can build a team and instil the values of Quality, Service and Cleanliness that set McDonald's apart from the competition. Your progress within McDonald's depends entirely on your individual performance. Ability, energy and commitment are the only criteria for promotion.

We believe that the best management skills are attained through actually performing the functions of a manager. All our initial training is completed on a one-to-one basis followed with classroom sessions and additional one-to-one, on-the-job training as necessary.

There is a carefully structured programme from trainee business manager through to area manager. In addition to the on-the-job and classroom training, we have our own management development programmes which guide our managers on the correct path.

There are three regional training centres; situated in Salford, Sutton Coldfield and East Finchley. Our national training centre is also based in East Finchley. Each centre possesses the latest in audio-visual training facilities, has classrooms holding up to 40 students, and an equipment laboratory.

We have a food hygiene induction system which, when linked with the training programme, provides the certificate in basic food hygiene as recognised by the EHO. In addition, the Management Development Programme is ratified by the MCI (Management Charter Initiative).

EMPLOYER FACTFILE

Total graduate vacancies **250**

Functions that McDonalds recruit graduates for

RETAILING

When to apply for graduate jobs

ROUND-THE-YEAR RECRUITMENT

There is no specific deadline for gradaute applications, but applying early is strongly recommended.

Universities McDonalds plan to visit during the 1999-2000 year

Please check with your local university careers service for full details of events.

Finding out more information

BROCHURE HOTLINE - London 0181 700 7007 or 0181 700 7888, Salford 0161 253 4229, Sutton Coldfield 0121 253 3588, Scotland 0141 207 6060

ADDRESS - McDonald's Restaurants Ltd, 11/59 High Road, East Finchley, London N2 8AW

"Did you know I started as a Graduate Trainee Manager? Now I run the company."

ANDREW TAYLOR - CHIEF EXECUTIVE.

It's a serious business.

Trainee Business Manager

And I'm not the only one on the Board who has worked their way up from the restaurants. We're that kind of company - we've always promoted from within, from crew level right up to senior management. So, if you thought McDonald's couldn't offer you a serious business career, think again.

First off, you should be setting your sights on restaurant management. Work hard and you could be there in two to three years, responsible for everything from marketing and finance to training and development. It's a considerable challenge but the training's thorough and we'll give you the time to learn our business from the ground up. After that, it's up to you how far you go.

We don't give this opportunity to just anyone. You'll have to convince us that you can deliver great customer service, demonstrate initiative, think on your feet and lead your team by setting the best example.

If you're serious about a business career, you should get in touch. Call our HR people in the South on 0181 700 7007 or 0181 700 7888, in the North on 0161 253 4229, in Scotland on 0141 207 6060 or in the Midlands on 0121 253 3588. Alternatively write to McDonald's Restaurants Ltd, 11-59 High Road, East Finchley, London N2 8AW. Please quote reference TE59.

A worldwide story of personal success

MARKS & SPENCER

Marks and Spencer has more than 442 stores worldwide and employs over 72,000 people. In addition to being one of the UK's leading retailers, we also operate a successful financial services business and a fast growing home shopping arm. Innovation during the last 12 months has been at a faster pace than at any other time in our history. And next year the pace of chance is likely to be even more furious.

We are re-branding and re-formatting many aspects of our business from store location and stock profile to merchandise and product offer. All of the time we're looking to build on our past success, while making certain we know exactly what tomorrow's customers want to buy.

Applicants must have a minimum grade C GCSE English and Maths plus a good degree in any subject. Exceptions are positions in Head Office Finance, where the minimum is 3 C's at A level plus a degree in any subject, and Food, Textile Technology and Selection where the candidate will need to have a relevant degree.

Graduate trainees spend time both in-store and at our Head Office. After an initial induction month, our in-store graduates will spend one month in each of the following areas: General Merchandise, Foods, Personnel and Finance. At each and every stage we will also focus on developing our graduates' managerial and technical skills. They will then spend seven months specialising in a chosen field - Commercial, Financial or Personnel.

At Head Office, training is a three-fold process. Initially we will bring our new graduates up to speed with the way we work and what will be expected of them. Following this, we focus on developing their technical and managerial skills, involving formal training, attachments, supplier visits or projects and first hand, front line experience.

After that, it's all about specialist development, giving graduates the opportunity to put all that theory into practice.

EMPLOYER FACTFILE

Total graduate vacancies   **80**

Functions Marks and Spencer recruit for

RETAILING	FINANCE
PURCHASING	HUMAN RESOURCES
GENERAL MANAGEMENT	IT

When to apply for graduate jobs

EARLY DEADLINE

Please check with your careers service.

Universities Marks and Spencer plan to visit during 1999-2000
Belfast (Queen's), Bristol, Durham, Manchester, Oxford, Reading, St Andrews, York

Please check with your local university careers service for full details of events.

Finding out more information

BROCHURE HOTLINE - 0171 268 8676

COMPANY WEBSITE - www.marks-and-spencer.com

ADDRESS - The Recruitment Department, Marks and Spencer PLC, Michael House, Baker Street, London W1A 1DN

The future is green,

not orange.

For further details on a career with Marks and Spencer, call our recruitment team on **0171 268 8676** or visit our web-site at:
www.marks-and-spencer.co.uk

Marks & Spencer is an equal opportunities employer

MARKS & SPENCER

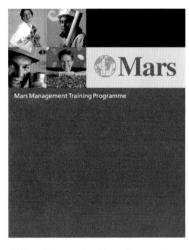
Mars Management Training Programme

Mars Incorporated is a world leader in each of its main businesses - branded snack foods, petcare products, main meal foods, automated payment systems and drinks vending. With over 140 sites in more than 60 countries worldwide, we employ some 30,000 associates and have an annual turnover in excess of £13 billion. Although a diversified multinational corporation, we are still privately owned and have total freedom to run and develop our business.

At Mars we do everything we can to make work a stimulating and satisfying place to be. Our business has an unusually small number of associates which means managers enjoy challenging work, diverse development opportunities and a high degree of accountability. Graduates who join us have real freedom to make a difference; doing real jobs with real responsibility.

The Mars Management Training Programme (MMTP) is designed to recruit and develop high calibre potential senior managers to meet local and international challenges. As a Trainee you will develop your managerial skills through a balance of on the job continuous learning, structured training, coaching and exposure to a variety of new challenges through early responsi-

bility. We are looking for graduates with any degree discipline.

At Mars we appreciate that there is strength in breadth and depth. In addition we will be offering Graduate opportunities on Corporate Development Programmes (CDP) for targeted career progression in the areas of Finance, Engineering, Software Engineering and IT.

We believe there is real strength in diversity and welcome graduates from a variety of ethnic backgrounds and cultures. Our approach to gradaute development offers challenging, stimulating and diverse opportunities to those with the ability to make the most of them.

EMPLOYER FACTFILE

Total graduate vacancies 25-30

Functions that Mars recruits graduates for

PURCHASING	LOGISTICS
SALES	RESEARCH & DEVELOPMENT
MARKETING	FINANCE
ENGINEERING	IT

Other opportunities are offered in the fields of Business Planning and Production Management.

When to apply for graduate jobs

EARLY DEADLINE - 4th NOVEMBER 1999

This deadline is for applications to the Mars Management Training Programme.

For Corporate Development Programmes, the closing date is 26th November 1999.

Universities Mars plan to visit during the 1999-2000 year
Bath, Birmingham, Bristol, Cambridge, Durham, Edinburgh, Leeds, Manchester, Newcastle, Nottingham, Oxford, Warwick

Please check with your local university careers service for full details of events.

Finding out more information

BROCHURE HOTLINE - 01753 514999

COMPANY EMAIL - mars.graduate@eu.effem.com

ADDRESS - Mars, Graduate Marketing, Dundee Road, Slough, Berks SL1 4JX

Mars – The hottest place to work

The Mars environment is one of constant innovation and change.

Our unique approach to graduate development is unrivalled in delivering challenge and opportunity.

Graduates who join us will have real freedom to make a difference.

 Pedigree Masterfoods
A Division of Mars U.K. Limited

 ISI Information Services International
A Division of Mars U.K. Ltd

MARS ELECTRONICS INTERNATIONAL

 FOUR SQUARE

 Mars

Mars

Mott MacDonald

Mott MacDonald is a world-class multi-disciplinary consultancy engaged in development touching many aspects of everyday life - from transport, energy, water and the environment to building, industry and communications.

We've been planning, driving and implementing some of the most demanding projects for over 100 years in over 100 countries, so our experience is hard to beat - demonstrated by landmark projects including Hong Kong's new airport terminal and Tsing Ma Bridge, LEGOLAND Windsor, Heathrow Express and the Channel Tunnel. We're currently busy on schemes including metros in Los Angeles and Bangkok, power stations in Singapore and Abu Dhabi and water supplies in Rawalpindi and Surabaya.

Applicants should have or expect to obtain a minimum of a 2.2 MEng or BEng degree in civil, structural, electrical, mechanical or building services engineering. We also welcome applications from those with an MSc in water resources, environmental engineering or transportation planning.

Mott MacDonald's Learning and Development scheme offers a balance of 'on the job' experience through assignments, to a variety of our specialist divisions and training via our comprehensive in-house course programme of over 60 topics.

An active mentoring system is able to offer support at all levels and on all subjects, especially career management.

To meet the future business needs of our international operations in all sectors, graduates must be versatile, flexible, and have a breadth of knowledge, skills and experience that can be utilised in any of our diverse client organisations. Our graduate programme is designed to equip graduates not only with the engineering expertise, but also the financial, commercial and managerial skills that are required in tomorrow's world.

Nestlé is the world's largest food company, and the UK is one of the largest markets in our global organisation. Founded over 130 years ago by Henri Nestlé in Vevey, Switzerland, we currently employ more than 230,000 people in over 80 countries around the world.

In the UK, Nestlé are leading manufacturers of a vast range of quality food and drink products sold under famous brand names, including Nescafé, Kit Kat, Aero, Crosse & Blackwell, and Shredded Wheat, and we are also leading suppliers to the restaurant and catering markets.

With around 13,000 employees at 20 locations nationwide and a turnover of over £1.7 billion, the company has a reputation that reflects high standards of quality, and commitment to both its employers and to the community.

Applicants are welcome from any degree discipline, although relevant degrees are required for the engineering and scientific and technical areas. Applicants should be likely to achieve or have achieved a 2:1 class degree and have above average A-levels or equivalents.

The majority of graduates will start at the company's headquarters in Croydon, or at the head office of the Nestlé Rowntree division in York. However, some vacancies will occur at our other national locations (particularly for human resources and manufacturing management) and your mobility

is therefore an important factor. To maximise your career progression, Nestlé would expect you to be adaptable and flexible, particularly in the early stages of your career development.

Early challenges and responsibility are key factors in the graduate training programme. During the first 18 months with the company, you will work within a specific division or corporate function, working on challenging assignments aimed at developing your potential and stretching your abilities.

In your first year you will participate in the Graduate Induction Programme which will provide you with the Nestlé company background knowledge and the personal and communication skills you need to operate successfully in the work environment. Support for professional qualifications will also be given where appropriate.

Beyond the graduate development programme, the emphasis of training shifts to increasing your business awareness and general management competencies.

As you progress you will discover that career development is not just about promotion; it is also about gaining experience in different parts of the business to broaden your commercial awareness.

Promotion within the company is dependent on your abilities and performance, and could take place cross-functionally or cross-divisionally.

Opportunities
of a lifetime.

The Nestlé Graduate Development Programme offers the chance to work on some of the UK's biggest and most exciting food brands – from Nescafé to Buitoni, Branston Pickle to Kit Kat, Nesquik to Milkybar, Crosse & Blackwell to Polo, Yorkie to Maggi.

The choice of discipline is also surprisingly varied: • Manufacturing Management • Engineering • Supply Chain • Scientific & Technical • Sales • Purchasing • Marketing • Information Systems • Finance • Human Resources • Marketing Research.

You'll find that Nestlé is a challenging and progressive environment to develop your career – and like our products, our Graduate Programme aims to make the very best!

For further details and a copy of our Graduate Opportunities brochure, see your Careers Advisor, or write to: Graduate Development Programme, Nestlé UK Ltd, St. George's House, Croydon, Surrey CR9 INR. Alternatively, you can send an e-mail to: nestlegrad@nestlegb.nestle.com or visit our website at www.nestlegrad.co.uk The closing date for applications is 24.11.99.

Nestlé

Nestlé makes the very best

NHS
MANAGEMENT
TRAINING
SCHEME

The National Health Service is the largest organisation in Britain. It employs over one million people, more than the top ten companies combined, and provides healthcare to over 57 million people.

While these statistics convey something of the scale of the NHS, they give little idea of its diversity. As well as providing healthcare through GPs, hospitals and emergency services, the NHS delivers long-term care for the elderly and mentally ill and support for the disabled and socially disadvantaged. It is proactive as well as reactive, promoting health education and supporting research, much of which has far-reaching consequences for the future of medical science.

Change is a constant feature of the NHS and the pace is quickening. Advances in medical technology, new thinking on primary care, tougher expenditure targets, higher public expectations - all this adds up to a complex, dynamic and challenging organisation to work in.

Our competence-based approach to assessment assures that as far as possible, applicants are considered on the evidence of their skills and competence, regardless of their personal backgrounds or circumstances. We welcome applications from a wide range of people. Current trainees reflect this and include men and women, mature candidates, NHS professionals, people with disabilities and from various ethnic

backgorunds. Whilst their circumstances vary considerably, what they have in common is a broad set of skills which meet our high standard and the potential and motivation to make a difference. To be eligible to apply for the scheme candidates should expect to have a degree or HND (in any subject) by September 2000.

Training will combine taking on early responsibility in a real management job whilst working towards a Postgraduate Diploma in Management. The scheme will provide experience of managing staff and budgets, business and service planning, operational management, and will provide a sound understanding of the way the NHS works.

The Scheme includes health service orientation (two contrasting work placements of nine months each); a management elective (an opportunity to spend time in another organisation to compare and contrast how things are done in the NHS); management education, in the form of modules and workshops taken alongside other trainees; support by a mentor who will provide guidance and feedback on progress; and support from a line manager who will help ensure that trainees develop the range of skills required.

By the end of the scheme, trainees should have gained a Postgraduate diploma in Management (with credit towards a Masters Degree), NVQ Level 4 and a certificate of graduation from MTS.

Management Training with the NHS

Could you handle **one of the most challenging management jobs** in Britain?

Joint Finance Process

West Lancs

Please see the
reference section
for details.

NHS

MANAGEMENT
TRAINING
SCHEME

For further information and an application form,
please send your details on a postcard to:
NHS MTS, Ref (TT100), The Manor House,
260 Ecclesall Road South, Sheffield, S11 9PS
You may want to visit our website at www.NHS-MTSandMESOL.demon.co.uk
Information is also available in large print, on audio cassette or in braille.
Call us on 0114 226 3000 for details.
Closing date for completed applications 3rd December 1999

Pfizer Central Research is the research and development division of Pfizer Inc., a global healthcare company. Our principle aim is to apply scientific knowledge to help people around the world enjoy longer, healthier and more productive lives. In 1998, we invested over $2 billion in research and development.

At our European Headquarters in Sandwich, a multimillion pound expansion has led to a state-of-the-art research campus. Our commitment to the careers and development of the 2,500 employees of European Central Research has never been stronger. This campus will almost double in size with new buildings by 2001.

We recruit graduates and postgraduates with the following degree disciplines: Biochemistry, Chemistry (organic and analytical), Chemical Engineering, Molecular Biology, Pharmacy, Pharmacology, Maths, Computer Science and Statistics. All graduates and postgraduates are expected to have a broad working knowledge around their degree discipline so that they are able to contribute from day one. (The only language skill we require is the ability to communicate clearly in English.)

Three-monthly reviews with your immediate superior will initially focus on how you are settling in. These two-way discussions then move towards work related issues, leading towards a more formal annual meeting where you discuss your goals for the year ahead and how you want to achieve them. From this you will be able to formulate your own development plan that includes personal goals, details of any external or internal training you may need and the support your supervisor can provide.

Total graduate vacancies   **40**

Functions Pfizer recruit for

RESEARCH & DEVELOPMENT

When to apply for graduate jobs

EARLY DEADLINE - 31st DECEMBER 1999

Universities Pfizer plan to visit during the 1999-2000 year

Please check with your local university careers service for full details of events.

Finding out more information

BROCHURE HOTLINE - 01304 648010

COMPANY WEBSITE - www.pfizer.co.uk/research

ADDRESS - University Resourcing Adviser, Pfizer Central Research, Ramsgate Road, Sandwich, Kent, CT13 9NJ

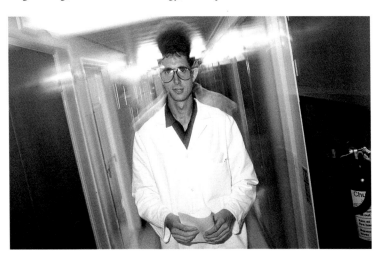

Life is our life's work

More than 17 million people around the world turn to our products every day to help them lead healthier, more productive lives.

http://www.pfizer.co.uk/recruit

Procter&Gamble

P rocter & Gamble is a dynamic, fast-moving multi-billion dollar business with operations all over the world. We sell over 300 household names and market leading brands such as Pampers, Fairy Liquid, Hugo Boss, Ariel and Pringles.

But our business is really about people, the 100,000 individuals who create a unique culture, strong sense of integrity and a never-ending creative drive.

We welcome applications from graduates in any discipline, except for Research & Development and some Product Supply roles where specific degrees are required. We are looking for graduates who have qualities such as Initiative, Leadership, Thinking and Problem Solving, Communication, Ability to Work with Others, Creativity and Innovation, Priority Setting and in some functions, Technical Mastery.

An individually tailored development plan provides the right mix of technical, project and management experience and is at the heart of our training strategy. This plan is developed through the following:

Ongoing one-to-one coaching from your manager. People care about your progress and performance, and the people who are coaching you are themselves assessed on your performance.

Regular review of performance, identifying your individual career development needs.

A formal introductory training famil-

iarises you with the company, our plans, policies, culture and work practices.

A corporate training programme helps shape the way you approach your responsibilities. Training covers areas such as competitive strategy, personal leadership, managing teams and developing coaching skills.

Functional training develops your technical skills and functional knowledge.

Promotion is based on contribution - the speed of your progress depends on you, your ability and your talent.

Procter & Gamble is a positive and very supportive environment. We will provice the training, experience and opportunities to ensure you develop an exciting and highly successful career. Your progress is important because our future depends on your success.

EMPLOYER FACTFILE

Total graduate vacancies   **130**

Functions Procter & Gamble recruit for

MARKETING	FINANCE
SALES	IT
ENGINEERING	LOGISTICS
RESEARCH & DEVELOPMENT	HUMAN RESOURCES

When to apply for graduate jobs

ROUND-THE-YEAR RECRUITMENT

There is no specific deadline for graduate applications, but the deadline for applying for a place on the Christmas Course is 1st November 1999. The company also offers places on Summer Internships.

Universities Procter & Gamble plan to visit during 1999-2000
Aberdeen, Aberystwyth, Aston, Bath, Belfast (Queen's), Birmingham, Bradford, Bristol, Cambridge, Cardiff, City, Durham, Edinburgh, Edinburgh, Exeter, Glasgow, Heriot-Watt, Lancaster, Leeds, London, Loughborough, Manchester, Newcastle, Nottingham, Oxford, Sheffield, Southampton, St Andrews, Stirling, Strathclyde, Surrey, Swansea, UMIST, Warwick, York

Finding out more information

BROCHURE HOTLINE - 0800 0565258.
COMPANY WEBSITE -
Email: recunitedkingdom.im@tg.com
www.pg.com/europe/oureg/uk.htm
ADDRESS - Corporate Recruitment, Procter & Gamble UK, St Nicholas Avenue, Gosforth NE99 1EE

PRICEWATERHOUSE COOPERS

ricewaterhouseCoopers is the world's leading professional services organisation.

Drawing on the knowledge and skills of more than 150,000 people in 150 countries, we help our clients solve complex business problems and measurably enhance their ability to build value, manage risk and improve performance.

We provide a full range of business advisory services to leading global, national and local companies and to public institutions.

Ours is an unparallelled fusion of culture and experience and with your unique qualities and abilities, you could be an important part of that. We recognise that our people are our

strength and are committed to helping them develop and grow, as we do.

Because we are growing, we have untold opportunities to develop you and help you achieve what you're capable of.

Working together, we can provide a framework for achieving success - indivudually and on a global scale - never before encountered.

Whichever office you're in, whichever country you're in, you would share common values with us - the drive and committment to make a real difference, not only in the local communities within which we live and work, but to the organisation the world over.

Applicants are required to have a minimum of 22 UCAS points and a good second class honours degree in any subject; some career options may require more specific degrees.

Academic achievement is, however, only part of the equation; we are looking for candidates with a high level of interpersonal skills, achievements and drive.

We offer training and development support for a number of professional qualifications - for more detailed information, please refer to our brochures and website.

Whatever route you take, we're with you every step of the way.

Graduates UK-wide

PRICEWATERHOUSE COOPERS ℞

Join us. Together we can change the world.

Just as no two mountains are identical, so too will the challenges and paths of your career differ from those around you. Which is why, as a recent graduate, you owe it to yourself to explore all your options and, most importantly, find out about the choices available to you on a graduate programme at PricewaterhouseCoopers.

In short, as your career climbs we can offer you the world. But then, as the largest professional services organisation around, that's not really surprising. What may surprise you is the sheer range of business areas open to you. From Assurance & Business Advisory Services, Tax & Legal Services to Management Consultancy, Financial Advisory Services, Global Risk Management Solutions and Actuarial, we have something that will suit you - whatever your long-term goals and ambitions.

What you'll also find is that we're a very different organisation. An organisation with a unique diversity of people and opportunities, and a supportive culture that deeply believes in you as an individual. An organisation capable of resolving business problems of a scale

and complexity never before encountered. An organisation with the wealth of resources necessary to enable you to make the most of yourself and your career with early responsibility, outstanding training and global development opportunities. You are our future. Your knowledge will prove one of our greatest assets and as you grow in experience and expertise you will be contributing to the growth of our business worldwide.

With highly competitive salaries, an extensive range of benefits, limitless career choices in various locations throughout the UK and a global stage on which to perform - we really are worth your while exploring. If you have a good degree, excellent academic record and an inquisitive mind - then maybe it's time you moved on to PricewaterhouseCoopers.

For more information, call our HR Service Centre on Freephone 0808 100 1500, quoting ref LB/01A or visit our website for more information, at www.pwcglobal.com/uk/graduate_careers/

www.pwcglobal.com

REUTERS

The Business of Information

To the world's financial markets, Reuters is the leading provider of real-time information and trading systems. To the 'world at large' Reuters is best known as the world's largest text and broadcast news agency. In its fast growing 'new-media' business Reuters provides information and news to the Internet.

Reuters is an exceptionally fast-moving company, operating in rapidly developing markets. A technical innovator, Reuters has its finger on the pulse of new and emerging technologies. For example, Reuters 'invented' e-commerce in the financial markets nearly 20 years ago!

Reuters presents an open window of opportunity for graduates with open minds. Early responsibility is yours for the taking. A career with Reuters has no geographical boundaries, nor limits of possibility. Our training is acknowledged to be amongst the best available.

Applicants should have a minimum of 24 UCAS points and have achieved or expect to achieve a minimum 2:1 degree in any discipline. Applicants need a consistent record of academic achievement as well as evidence that you work well, and have achieved results, through and with others, demonstrable international outlook; innovative thinking and inspired by the future; the ability to adapt to new challenges, and constantly expect - and can deal with - the unexpected.

Our Business Management programme aims to ensure the effective coordination of three key disciplines - marketing, product development and front-line account management - and all on a global scale.

The Technical Management programme develops specialists who deploy market-leading solutions globally. You will work at the leading edge of technology with vendors, strategic partners, global standards bodies and customers. In the final analysis, the quality of our IT determines the success of our business.

Reuters needs to derive maximum value from all the resources at its disposal and the Finance programme equips you with the relevant skills. You will be given study leave and financial assistance to gain a professional qualification, such as the Chartered Institute of Management Accountants.

Our Journalism programme is designed to turn graduates into internationally experienced, multi-skilled journalists with the versatility to write for the financial markets, screen services, the news media and the Internet 'public'. Throughout, you develop Reuters standards for reporting - fast, accurate and free from bias. All our programmes are likely to involve overseas assignments.

As well as the Graduate Development Programmes, we offer Reuters Direct - immediate entry into a job - where entrants rapidly become effective members of the team, starting on the road to becoming a future expert in their field.

EMPLOYER FACTFILE

Total graduate vacancies   **50**

Functions that Reuters recruit graduates for

IT	MARKETING
SALES	MEDIA
FINANCE	RESEARCH & DEVELOPMENT

When to apply for graduate jobs

EARLY DEADLINE - 30th DECEMBER 1999

The above deadline is for graduate programmes. For Reuters Direct, the deadline is 30th April 2000.

Universities Reuters plan to visit during the 1999-2000 year
Bristol, Cambridge, Durham, Edinburgh, Exeter, Manchester/UMIST, Oxford, St Andrews
Please check with your local university careers service for full details of events.

Finding out more information

BROCHURE HOTLINE - 0207 542 7162

COMPANY WEBSITE -
www.reuters.com/careers/graduate

ADDRESS - 85 Fleet Street, London EC4P 4AJ

New generations. New technologies. New challenges.

Globalisation is removing boundaries. Events and alliances move financial markets. News triggers reaction and transaction. Reuters delivers. Every second of every day. Information, prices, market intelligence... in perpetual motion. Look to the future with Reuters. A global business. A non-stop challenge.

For further insight into the world of Reuters, our graduate brochure is available from our 24-hour Graduate Recruitment hotline on 0171-542 7162 or our internet site. www.reuters.com/careers/graduate

REUTERS

The Business of Information

Rolls-Royce

Rolls-Royce is one of the most famous names in engineering, leading the world in gas turbine technology.

Rolls-Royce plc serves customers in the civil aerospace, defence and energy sectors of international markets and has facilities in 14 countries. The gas turbine technology of Rolls-Royce generates 95% of the group's sales and has created one of the broadest product ranges of aero engines in the world today.

Rolls-Royce designs and manufactures the engines that power many of the world's most famous civil and military aircraft and employs some 40,000 people worldwide.

Rolls-Royce recruits a broad range of disciplines but always looks for people it believes have the potential to become leaders or acknowledged experts in their field. Some will want to be managers of people, others will choose to specialise in a particular area. Whatever their disciplines, graduate recruits need to demonstrate high intellect and a broad business understanding.

Graduate recruitment at Rolls-Royce reflects the international nature of the company and a significant proportion of trainees are recruited from outside the UK.

The Rolls-Royce graduate training programmes are designed to equip graduates with the skills and experience they need to get their careers off to a

flying start. The programme includes a number of attachments in different areas of the company. Each attachment is likely to last between eight and 12 weeks and involves real work and responsibility for achieving an agreed, measurable set of performance objectives. A training officer will work with each graduate to structure an individual schedule of attachments and training activities.

Most programmes last between 12 and 18 months and incorporate a range of professional and personal development activities. At the end of the training period the first appointment will depend on a combination of the graduates personal preferences and the recommendations of the managers and supervisors.

Rolls-Royce has strong links with a number of professional institutions and is committed to helping employees gain additional professional qualifications.

Graduate development is characterised by a culture of professionalism, an emphasis on global and business awareness, career planning, the development of both general managers and specialists, and development related to performance and aptitude.

There are many opportunities to work overseas and to move between the businesses. The increasingly global nature of business at Rolls-Royce actually requires a commitment to mobility for those aspiring to reach senior positions.

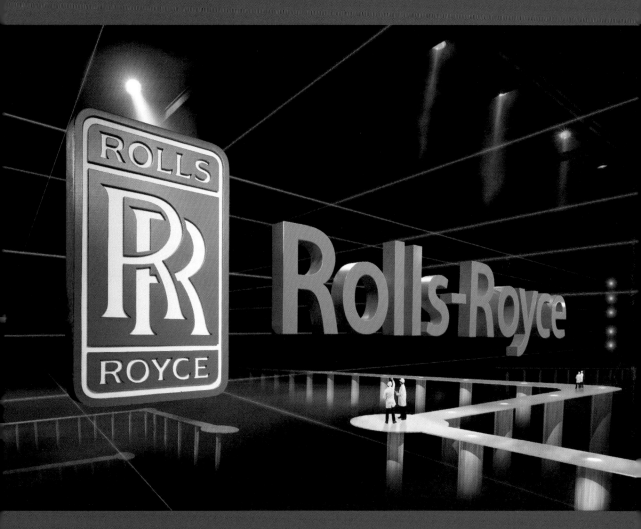

ROYAL NAVY

The Royal Navy is responsible for the strategic defence of the UK and its dependent territories. Imagine yourself flying a fixed-wing, fast jet aircraft or going hundreds of fathoms deep surveying the seabed in a nuclear submarine, being the warfare officer of a stealth frigate or working on a state of the art technology such as advanced sonar systems.

The Royal Navy needs people with a wide range of skills of which seamanship os only one, equally important are engineers, warfare officers, logistics experts and nurses, to name but a few.

The Royal Navy trains you to carry out a specific role to work as part of a team. You could be involved in many of the humanitarian relief operations around the world after the wake of natural disasters such as volcanic operations, earthquakes or hurricanes.

The Royal Navy is also involved in other peactime activities such as patrolling for drug smugglers and search and rescue operations.

We are seeking graduates with good leadership skills and initiative who are up to the challenge of being in charge of twenty men after one year, responsible for their training development, as well as personal issues that may arise.

The Royal Navy offers equal opportunities, good pay (after one year you will be earning a minimum of £20,000, rising to £26,000 after two years) and a generous holiday allowance. Officers may be selected for fully funded postgraduate study.

Graduate engineers will be given an additional £4,000 restrospective bursary on joining.

The minimum commitment is three years although this may vary according to specialisation, though we are committed to providing you with a long term rewarding career should you be up to the challenge.

EMPLOYER FACTFILE

Total graduate vacancies **450**

Functions that the Royal Navy recruit graduates for

ENGINEERING	LOGISTICS

Other opportunities are also available in Warfare, Medical and the Fleet Air Arm.

When to apply for graduate jobs

ROUND-THE-YEAR RECRUITMENT

There is no specific deadline for graduate applications, but applying early is strongly recommended.

Universities that the Royal Navy plan to visit during 1999-2000

Please check with your local university careers service for full details of events.

Finding out more information

BROCHURE HOTLINE - 0345 300123, quoting reference BL210

COMPANY WEBSITE -
www.royal-navy.mod.uk/careers

ADDRESSES - Captain John Wotton, RN CCareers Service Dept BL210, Freepost GL672, Cirencester, Gloucs, GL7 1BR

GO FARTHER STRIPES

By becoming an officer in the Royal Navy you won't only go far in life, you'll get there faster. You will be trained by the best instructors in the world, allowing you to explore a wide variety of jobs in warfare, logistics, engineering and aviation. After just one year you could be in charge of over 20 men and women who will look to you as their mentor as well as their leader. Naturally such responsibility is handsomely rewarded (you will be earning £26,000 after just 2 years). And if you want to become an officer and a graduate that's great. We sponsor hundreds of students through university every year. So you can actually start furthering your career before you have even joined up. For further information on careers in the Royal Navy call the telephone number below quoting reference BL210.

Schlumberger

Schlumberger is a global technical company whose key activities are in Oilfield Services, Test Systems and Measurement Technologies.

"I agree to disburse to my sons Conrad and Marcel the funds necessary for research study in view of determining the nature of the subsurface. The field of activity is vast enough to satisfy their inventive genius by its investigation; they must devote themselves to it entirely. The scientific interest in research must take precedence over financial interest."

This is an extract from the text of an eighty-year-old agreement between Pierre Schlum-berger and his two sons. It acted as the starting point to a chain of events which has led Schlumberger to become one of the most successful organisations in the world, with more than 60,000 people of more than 100 nationalities in as many countries. The company operates in fields as diverse as seismic data acquisition and smart card design, and was selected by *Wired* magazine as one of their 40 companies 'building the new economy'.

We recruit predominately technical people, and we are looking for people who don't leave university wanting a quiet life but instead want to be challenged right from day one. One year from now you could be solely responsible for a multi-million dollar operation. You will be backed up by our world-renowned training programmes but nevertheless you will be tested to the limit.

Of course with the challenges come opportunities. Our borderless careers programme means that the only limits to your development will be your abilities and ambition. We have a strong ethic of promotion from within (our current Chairman, Euan Baird, joined us direct from Cambridge University) and of providing our employees with as much responsibility as they are ready to handle.

Schlumberger has an unparalleled reputation for the quality of its training programmes. Most often the initial training will be highly structured. Within the Oilfield part of the group intensive technical training is combined with on-the-job work with your mentor. Within eight-months we expect you to be able to handle a team and project on your own. Later training will be tailored to your needs and development, by the end of 30 months you will have the skills necessary to make your first 'borderless' move.

Training is a combination of intensive sessions at our training centres, on-line and CD-Rom based modules and on-the-job learning. Your progress will be continuously monitored by your manager and the supporting technical staff.

Continuous development is necessary for your career with Schlumberger, and support is provided whether through internal professional development programmes or external further education. You will never stop learning.

EMPLOYER FACTFILE

Total graduate vacancies   **100**

Functions that Schlumberger recruit graduates for

ENGINEERING   RESEARCH & DEVELOPMENT
IT

When to apply for graduate jobs
ROUND-THE-YEAR RECRUITMENT

There is no specific deadline for graduate applications, but applying early is strongly recommended.

Universities Schlumberger plan to visit during 1999-2000
Bristol, Cambridge, Durham, Edinburgh, Glasgow, Heriot-Watt, Leeds, Liverpool, London, Loughborough, Manchester, Newcastle, Southampton, Strathclyde, UMIST

Please check with your local university careers service for full details of events.

Finding out more information

BROCHURE HOTLINE - 01223 325214

COMPANY WEBSITE - www.slb.com/recr/uk

ADDRESS - High Cross, Madingley Road, Cambridge CB3 0EL

You'll *stop* being a *student*

but *why* stop *learning?*

Schroders

With our head office in the heart of the City and a presence in the financial markets of 35 countries worldwide, Schroders is one of the world's most successful investment banking and asset management groups. We have £119 billion under management and a market value of £3 billion. In the UK, we have more client FTSE-100 companies than any of our competitors.

Never complacent, Schroders constantly seeks new ways to innovate and develop value-added services for our clients. Just as there is no standard way of doing things at Schroders, so there is no typical person who works here.

We pride ourselves on a culture where individual thinkers flourish while benefitting from the support of strong team-based structures.

Opportunities exist for talented graduates in Investment Management - Asset Management and Marketing; Investment Banking - Corporate Finance, Securities and Financial Markets (Proprietary Trading, Structuring Group, Financing and Sales); Financial Control; Group Risk; IT and Human Resources.

We need graduates with an impressive academic record - applicants should have at least 24 UCAS points (20 for those applying for IT positions) or overseas equivalent and have achieved or expect to achieve a minimum 2:1 degree.

We want creative but constructive thinkers, confident communicators who can liaise with clients and colleagues at all levels, individuals who are motivated by the chance to take real responsibility at an early stage.

Our three-month Graduate Training Programme is carefully designed to equip individuals with the skills pertinent to their chosen business area. Initially, graduates will be provided with a comprehensive overview of the organisation and an insight into the core products and markets across the group. Divisional specific training will then follow, focusing on detailed and technical analysis of the processes, tools and techniques used in the different business areas. Finally, a week-long outward bound course in the Lake District consolidates newly-learnt skills and ensures the formation of enduring friendships.

Ongoing training is an essential part of our culture and will vary within the different divisions. Whatever your role however, you will be working with a small team interacting daily with key senior figures in the bank which will ensure exposure to the full scope of the bank's activities at the highest levels.

At Schroders, you will find an environment where your personal qualities are prized on a par with your intelligence and hard work, and self-motivation is rewarded with rapid advancement.

It's time to consider Schroders

You've set your heart on a career in the City. You're prepared for the challenge ahead - and you're willing to put the hours in to succeed. You're familiar with financial products. You're unfazed by the technical jargon. It's now just a question of selecting the company that is right for you...

It's time to take a serious look at Schroders. Our success can be attributed to a unique business strategy and culture: while others race to have a presence in every market, we hand-pick profitable sectors where our experience is unequalled.

Our environment is characterised by respect, co-operation, professionalism and intellectual agility. We pride ourselves on a working atmosphere which is team-focused, supportive and egalitarian. We need some 50-60 graduates - dynamic team players who can fit into client-facing roles across all business areas including:

Investment Management
Asset Management and Marketing

Investment Banking
Corporate Finance
Securities – Equity Research and Sales
Financial Markets - Proprietary Trading,
Structuring, Sales and Financing

Financial Control
Group Risk
Information Technology
Human Resources

We need graduates with an impressive academic record - at least 24 UCAS points (20 for IT) or overseas equivalent and achievement/expectation of a 2:i degree. We want creative but constructive thinkers... confident communicators who can liaise with clients and colleagues at all levels... individuals motivated by the chance to take real responsibility at an early stage.

Please note that we also offer work experience opportunities to penultimate year students on our Summer Intern Scheme. The same criteria apply.

It's now time to find out more by visiting our website at: **www.schroders.com/graduaterecruitment**

A brochure and application form can be obtained from either your careers service or by calling Freephone 0800 282 664 ext. 6206.

Applications for 2000 Graduate entry should reach

your life...
your move

Individual
contribution...
team success

STANDARD LIFE

You're one of the brightest students in your year, and you're on the look-out for a career with a dynamic financial services company that will encourage your ambition, offer you excellent training and give you the opportunities you deserve. You're working hard to get your 2:1 or 1st and you're prepared to offer 100% commitment. But you're looking for a good deal in return.

Starting out on a brilliant career with Standard Life, you'll join a graduate training programme that will introduce you to every aspect of a forward-looking financial services company. Training and development activities vary depending on your chosen specialism, and are a mix of in-house training, external courses and work assignments.

You'll also be assigned an individual coach. In addition, you'll be encouraged to study for a professional qualification and given all the support you need to achieve your goal.

You'll be working on real projects, so you must be able to work with all types of people, use your initiative and work as part of a team. In return for your commitment, you can expect a competitive salary and attractive financial sector benefits package that reflect your skills.

Based in Edinburgh, you'll be living and working in one of the most exciting, cosmopolitan cities in the UK, a European Capital and home to the new Scottish Parliament. A city with a colourful cultural and social scene, a fantastic life experience.

EMPLOYER FACTFILE

Total graduate vacancies **30**

Functions that Standard Life recruits graduates for

ACCOUNTANCY	HUMAN RESOURCES
GENERAL MANAGEMENT	IT

When to apply for graduate jobs

EARLY DEADLINE - 31st JANUARY 2000

Universities Standard Life plan to visit during 1999-2000
Aberdeen, Cambridge, Durham, Edinburgh, Glasgow, Glasgow Caledonian, Heriot-Watt, Napier, Oxford, Paisley, St Andrews, Stirling, Strathclyde, Warwick
Please check with your local university careers service for full details of events.

Finding out more information

BROCHURE HOTLINE - 0131 245 0587

COMPANY WEBSITE -
www.individuals.co.uk *(for graduate information)*
www.standardlife.co.uk *(for company information)*

ADDRESS - Graduate Recruitment Team, Standard Life House, 30 Lothian Road, Edinburgh EH1 2DH

Unilever

A global business employing a quarter of a million people with a turnover of £27 billion, generating a £2.9 billion profit, Unilever is behind many of the world's best known branded and packaged goods in foods and home and personal care. Our aim is to meet the everyday needs of people everywhere.

Unilever in the UK consists of nine operating companies: on the foods side Arkady Craigmillar, Birds Eye Wall's and Van den Bergh Foods, and on the home and personal care side Calvin Klein, Elida Fabergé, Elizabeth Arden, Lever Brothers and Unipath. Key brands include Persil, Flora, Magnum, cK one, Visible Difference and Clearblue. The final company in the UK portfolio is DiverseyLever, one of the world's leading cleaning and hygiene specialists.

Our research and development teams are based in six state-of-the-art laboratories, two of which are in the UK at Sharnbrook (Bedfordshire) and Port Sunlight (Merseyside). Complemented by a network of 71 innovation centres, they focus not only on specific categories, like ice cream, laundry and skin care, but also on their own region. In 1998 we spent £600 million on research and development. To protect the proprietary nature of our research activity, we filed 345 patent applications.

We need to recruit graduates of the highest quality, who have the potential to reach senior management, on to the Unilever Companies Management Development Scheme (UCMDS). Personal attributes such as the ability to inspire and motivate others, the willingness to put the needs of the team first, the skill to see right to the heart of a problem and to arrive at innovative solutions are paramount. Your offer will be from one of the Unilever operating companies.

Starting salaries for autumn 1999 ranged from £20 to £24k per annum, depending on postgraduate qualifications, depth of relevant experience and performance at final assessment. Benefits include pension scheme and life assurance, 25 days holiday, the opportunity to defer for a year and an advance of a month's salary paid on joining to help with initial expenses.

You will get the chance to exercise responsibility early in your career, attaining your first management position within 2 years. This means that, during your first few years, you will receive job related training, placements and projects, as well as receiving regular informal feedback and formal appraisal of your performance.

Unilever training and development focuses on individual needs by working with each employee to develop a performance development plan. You will also be encouraged to study for relevant professional qualifications e.g. chartered status for manufacturing and supply chain trainees and CIMA is essential for finance trainees.

Unilever brands touch the lives of over half the families on the planet.

Unilever

To maintain this success we need to attract graduates of the highest calibre.

Unilever Companies Management Development Scheme is widely regarded as one of the best routes into management in the world.

*Unilever Companies **Management Development** Scheme*

To find out more about Unilever and UCMDS call our hotline: 0541 543 550 or visit our website: www.ucmds.com

www.ucmds.com   Be part of it.   hotline: 0541 543 550

United Biscuits

United Biscuits is a dynamic international food manufacturer. We're a major producer of branded snackfoods, and our vision is to be the best biscuit company in Europe operating from a strong UK base.

Founded in 1948, we now have an annual turnover of £1.7bn, with operations in 22 countries across Europe and East Asia. Countries of operation include the UK, France, the Netherlands, Belgium, Germany, Sweden, Finland, Denmark, Norway, Malaysia, China and Japan. Well known brands in the UK include McVitie's Jaffa Cakes, HobNobs, Hula Hoops, McCoy's, Go Ahead! and Penguin. Throughout the 1990s we've grown our international biscuit business to the point where the majority of our sales come from outside the UK, and it's these international markets that will drive our future growth.

We're looking for people with the potential to reach the most senior management levels within 10 years of joining our organisation. Whilst we expect our recruits to have a strong academic background, we place as much emphasis on their ability to put this learning into practice: so we also look for outstanding leadership potential, coupled with strong self-development and team-working skills. We expect all research & development, new product development and technical services graduates to have the relevant scientific background, but accept applicants with any degrees (with a minimum of a 2:2) in all other functions.

Our 'Understanding Business Programme' uses off-site training modules to allow young managers to develop their knowledge of the behaviours used by our most successful managers: they then complete on-site assignments that allow them to focus this learning onto real business scenarios.

The programme lasts for around 2-3 years and is run by Henley Management College, one of the UK's top business education providers: for successful delegates, it leads to a Diploma in Management. We also provide all relevant functional training, such as CIMA for finance graduates, IPD for human resources people, our in-house 'Generating Excellence in Marketing' programme for marketeers, and our PC-based technical development programme.

All graduates have real roles from day one, and are given the support to achieve the demanding results that are expected of them.

As our application process is based around our recruitment website, we suggest that if you're interested in finding out more, you visit us at www.unitedbiscuits.co.uk. This will give you a more detailed insight into our company, the training we offer and the jobs you might expect to do with us.

EMPLOYER FACTFILE

Functions that United Biscuits recruit graduates for

FINANCE	HUMAN RESOURCES
SALES	RESEARCH & DEVELOPMENT
LOGISTICS	IT
MARKETING	PURCHASING

Opportunities are also available in Operations Management, New Product Development and Technical Services.

When to apply for graduate jobs

EARLY DEADLINE

Please refer to website for further details. United Biscuits may also be conducting a summer round of recruitment - please check with your local university careers service for details.

Universities United Biscuits plan to visit during 1999-2000
Aston, Birmingham, Bristol, Cambridge, Cardiff, Durham, Leeds, London, Manchester, Newcastle, Nottingham, Oxford, Reading, Sheffield, Strathclyde, UMIST

Please check with your local university careers service for full details of events.

Finding out more information

BROCHURE HOTLINE - 0800 801065

COMPANY WEBSITE - www.unitedbiscuits.co.uk

ADDRESS - Church Road, West Drayton, UB7 7PR

ABBEY NATIONAL PLC
Midsummer Boulevard, 201 Grafton Gate East, Milton Keynes MK9 1AN

ALLEN & OVERY
One New Change, London EC4M 9QQ

BANK OF ENGLAND
1-2 Bank Buildings, Princes Street, London EC2R 8EU

BANK OF SCOTLAND
Staff Training Centre, 58 St Albans Road, Edinburgh EH9 2LX

BARCLAYS BANK PLC
54 Lombard Street, London EC3P 3AH

BBC
16 Langham Street, London W1A 1AA

THE BOOTS COMPANY PLC
D31 Building, 1 Thane Road, Nottingham NG2 3AA

THE BOSTON CONSULTING GROUP
Devonshire House, Mayfair Place, London W1X 5FH

BP AMOCO PLC
Britannic House, 1 Finsbury Circus, London EC2M 7BA

BRITISH SUGAR PLC
Oundle Road, Peterborough PE2 9QU

BT PLC
81 Newgate Street, London EC1A 7AJ

CABLE & WIRELESS COMMUNUCATIONS LTD
Caxton Way, Watford Business Park, Watford WD1 8XH

CAPITAL ONE
18 Hanover Square, London W1R 9DA

CITIBANK NA
336 Strand, London WC2R 1HB

CIVIL SERVICE
Capita RAS Ltd, Innovation Court, New Street, Basingstoke RG21 7BJ

CLIFFORD CHANCE
200 Aldersgate Street, London EC1A 4JJ

CREDIT SUISSE FIRST BOSTON
One Cabot Square, Canary Wharf, London E14 4JQ

DATA CONNECTION LTD
100 Church Street, Enfield, Middlesex EN2 6BQ

DELOITTE & TOUCHE
Cedric House, 8-9 East Harding Street, London EC4A 3PA

DEUTSCHE BANK
Winchester House, 1 Great Winchester Street, London EC2 2DB

DRUID
Thompson House, 420 Thames Valley Park Drive, Thames Valley Park, Reading RG6 1PU

EDS LTD
4 Poundwood Avenue, Stockley Park, Uxbridge, Middlesex UB11 1BQ

ERNST & YOUNG
1 Lambeth Palace Road, London SE1 7EU

ESSO & EXXON GROUP
Administration Building, Fawley Refinery, Southampton SO45 1TX

EUROPEAN UNION
200 Rue de la Loi, B1049, Brussels, Belguim

EVERSHEDS
Senator House, 85 Queen Victoria Street, London EC4V 4JL

FOREIGN AND COMMONWEALTH OFFICE
1 Palace Street, London SW1E 5HE

GLAXOWELLCOME UK LTD
Stockley Park West, Uxbridge, Middlesex UB11 1BT

GOLDMAN SACHS
1 Carter Lane, London EC4V 5ER

HEWLETT PACKARD
Cain Road, Bracknell, Berkshire RG12 1HN

J SAINSBURY PLC
Stamford House, Stamford Street, London SE1 9LL

JOHN LEWIS PARTNERSHIP
Department of Personnel, 171 Victoria Street, London SW1E 5NN

KPMG
8 Salisbury Square, London EC4Y 8BB

LINKLATERS AND ALLIANCE
1 Silk Street, London EC2V 8HQ

MARAKON ASSOCIATES
Grand Buildings, 1-3 Strand, London WC2N 5HP

MCKINSEY & COMPANY
1 Jermyn Street, London SW1Y 4UH

MERRILL LYNCH EUROPE PLC
25 Ropemaker Street, London EC2Y 9LY

MICROSOFT LTD
Microsoft Campus, Thames Valley Park, Reading RG6 1WG

MITCHELL MADISON GROUP
Portland House, Stag Place, London SW1E 5ZT

NORTEL NETWORKS PLC
Maidenhead Office Park, Westacott Way, Maidenhead, Berkshire SL6 3QH

NORTON ROSE
Kempson House, Camomile Street, London EC3A 7AN

OLIVER, WYMAN & CO
1 Neal Street, Covent Garden, London WC2H 9PU

OVE ARUP & PARTNERS
13 Fitzroy Street, London W1P 6BQ

P&O NEDLLOYD LTD
Beagle House, Braham Street, London E1 8EP

PA CONSULTING GROUP
123 Buckingham Palace Road, London SW1W 9SR

PEUGEOT MOTOR COMPANY PLC
PO Box 25, Humber Road, Coventry CV3 1BD

PHILIPS ELECTRONIC UK LTD
The Philips Centre, 420-430 London Road, Croydon, Surrey CR9 3QR

POLICE SERVICE
Room 549, The Home Office, 50 Queen Anne's Gate, London SW1H 9AT

RAF
Directorate of Recruiting, RAF Cranwell, Sleaford, Lincolnshire NG34 8HBB

ROYAL BANK OF SCOTLAND
52 West Register Street, Edinburgh EH2 2AA

SAATCHI & SAATCHI
80 Charlotte Street, London W1A 1AQ

SALOMON SMITH BARNEY
Victoria Plaza, 111 Buckingham Palace Road, London SW1W 0SB

SHELL INTERNATIONAL
Shell Centre, London SE1 7NA

SLAUGHTER & MAY
35 Basinghall Street, London EC2V 5DB

SMITHKLINE BEECHAM PLC
New Horizons Court, Great West Road, Brentford, Middlesex TW8 9EP

SONY UNITED KINGDOM LTD
The Heights, Brooklands, Weybridge, Surrey KT13 0XW

TESCO STORES LTD
PO Box 18, Delamere Road, Cheshunt, Herts EN8 9FL

VIRGIN MANAGEMENT LTD
Head Office, 120 Campden Hill Road, London W8 7AR

WALKERS SNACK FOODS LTD
1600 Arlington Business Park, Theale, Reading, Berkshire RG7 4SA

WARBURG DILLON READ
100 Liverpool Street, London EC2M 2RH

These details generally refer to the organisation's head office in the UK. For details of their graduate recruitment offices and possible vacancies, please check the relevant files at your local University Careers Service.